Antonia Clare
JJ Wilson

speakout

Pre-intermediate
Workbook with key

CONTENTS

CONTENTS

VOCABULARY free time

1 Match phrases 1–10 with pictures A–J.

1 go shopping _____
2 go on holiday _____
3 spend time with your family _____
4 spend money _____
5 eat out _____
6 eat with friends _____
7 have time off _____
8 have a barbecue _____
9 play volleyball _____
10 play the guitar _____

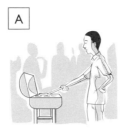
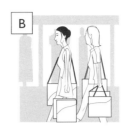

GRAMMAR question forms

2 Put the words in the correct order to make questions.

1 is / birthday / when / your ?
When is your birthday?

2 English / time / lessons / your / start / what / do ?
_____

3 friends / cook for / often / you / how / your / do ?
_____

4 in / many / there / family / how / are / your / people ?
_____

5 come / does / mother / where / your / from ?
_____

6 meat / don't / eat / you / why ?
_____

7 glasses / in / of / many / day / water / you / how / drink / a / do ?
_____

8 is / where / the / classroom ?
_____

9 your / best / see / did / friend / when / last / you ?
_____

10 go / shopping / where / did / you ?
_____

3 Write questions for the answers. Use the question words in the box.

~~where~~ what why when who how often which how many what

1 *Where are you from?* _____
I'm from Poland.

2 _____ ?
I'm a student.

3 _____ with ?
I live with my friend Olga.

4 _____ ?
Only two people live in the house, Olga and me.

5 _____ ?
In our free time we like to go to the cinema, or go out with friends. We both love reading, too.

6 _____ ?
We go to the cinema about once a week.

7 _____ ?
I'm studying English because I would like to work in this country.

8 _____ ?
I'm in class 2A, Pre-intermediate.

9 _____ ?
I started learning English when I was at school.

READING

4A Read the text and match headings A–F with paragraphs 1–6.

A Call a friend

B Just smile

C Do something nice for someone

D Be active

E Do that difficult job

F Plan for some future fun

Make Yourself Happy:

SIX TIPS TO MAKE YOU HAPPIER IN THE NEXT HOUR

You can make yourself happier starting now. In the next hour, do as many of these things as possible. Each thing you do will help you to feel happier.

1 _____: stand up and walk around while you talk on the phone. Or go for a quick ten-minute walk outside. Doing exercise gives you energy and makes you feel better.

2 _____: arrange to meet someone for lunch or send an email to a friend you haven't seen for a long time. Having good relationships with other people is one of the things that makes us happy, so stay in touch with your friends.

3 _____: answer a difficult email, or call to make that dentist's appointment. Do it now, don't wait. Cross something off your list of 'things to do' to give yourself energy.

4 _____: order a book you want to read, plan a trip to a museum or a night out with friends. If you look forward to doing something fun in the future, it will make you feel happy right now.

5 _____: buy someone flowers, carry their bag, tell them they look nice. Do good, feel good – this really works. If you do something nice for someone, it makes you feel better.

6 _____: even when you don't feel happy, always try to smile. Put a smile on your face right now. It will make you feel better.

Tick things off the list when you do them. Do you feel happier yet?

B Read the text again. Are the sentences true (T) or false (F)?

1 Doing exercise makes you tired. ____

2 Having friends is an important part of being happy. ____

3 Doing a difficult job uses all your energy. ____

4 Planning fun things to do can make you happy. ____

5 If you do something to make someone else feel good, you will feel good yourself.

6 Smiling too much can make you feel bad. ____

C Read the text again and answer questions 1–6 below.

1 What should you do when you talk on the phone?

_____

2 Why is it important to stay in touch with friends?

_____

3 What kinds of jobs are on a 'things to do' list?

_____

4 Why is it a good idea to organise something fun to do in the future?

_____

5 How will you feel if you buy someone flowers or carry their bag?

_____

6 What happens when you smile?

_____

D Complete the definitions with phrases from the text.

1 look _____ to something: be excited about something which will happen in the future

2 have good _____ with people: be friendly with these people

3 _____ things off a list: mark items on a list when you do them

4 stay in _____ with people: contact people regularly (by phone, email, etc.)

5 doing _____: do some kind of activity like walking or playing tennis

VOCABULARY relationships

1 Complete the story with the words and phrases in the box below.

~~have a girlfriend~~   got on well   met   got divorced
fell in love   got married   argued   accepted
got back together again   asked her to marry him

When Harry met Sally ...

1 Harry didn't *have a girlfriend*.

2 He _____ Sally in a café. They _____.

3 They _____.

4 He _____ and she _____.

5 They _____.

6 They _____.

7 Then they _____.

8 And finally, they _____.

GRAMMAR past simple

2A Mark the verbs in the box regular (R) or irregular (I).

fall *I*   argue   happen   ask   decide   find   get   know
look   meet   say   spend   stay   study   think   travel

B Write the past simple form of the irregular verbs.

fall – fell _____

3 Complete the story with the past simple form of the verbs in the box.

become   decide   meet   send   get   ask   have
not tell   start   arrive   live   talk

Ten years ago, before it was fashionable to date on the internet, I ^{1}_____ a Swedish lady in a chat room. We ^{2}_____ on well from the first minute we ^{3}_____ chatting, and she soon ^{4}_____ my girlfriend. The only problem was that I ^{5}_____ in the UK, and she was in Sweden. For a couple of years, we ^{6}_____ a long-distance relationship. We ^{7}_____ on the phone and ^{8}_____ emails to each other. We ^{9}_____ our friends how we met because we were embarrassed. After a while, I ^{10}_____ to leave England and move to Sweden. When I ^{11}_____, I ^{12}_____ her to marry me. Now, we are happily married and we have four children. I think online dating is fantastic. I met my wife because of it.

4 Complete the sentences with the past simple form of the verb in brackets.

1 A: Where _____ (stay)?
   B: We _____ (find) a hotel near the station.

2 We _____ (eat) in the hotel restaurant and the food was delicious.

3 Mara and Steve _____ (not have) a barbecue on Sunday because it rained all day.

4 We _____ (go) to the cinema, but I _____ (not like) the film. I _____ (think) it was really boring.

5 I _____ (spend) the weekend studying because I've got an exam tomorrow.

6 He _____ (be) really busy yesterday so he _____ (not have) time to call you.

7 She _____ (write) a long letter explaining the problem, but her boyfriend still _____ (not understand).

8 They _____ (give) her some beautiful flowers for her birthday.

9 A: What time _____ (get) back home last night?
   B: At about midnight.

10 I _____ (start) this job four years ago when I _____ (move) to Rome.

5A Say the words and circle the verb ending which sounds different.

1 played	stayed	tried	ended
2 asked	kissed	arrived	talked
3 finished	decided	pretended	wanted
4 studied	happened	invented	stayed
5 walked	helped	stopped	started

B ▶ 1.1 Listen and check.

LISTENING

6A ▶ 1.2 Listen to the story of Elvis and Priscilla Presley. Number the pictures in the correct order 1–6.

A

B

C

D

E

F

B Listen again. Answer the questions.

1 How old was Priscilla when she met Elvis?

_____

2 Where were they?

_____

3 How did they keep in touch when he was in the USA?

_____

4 When did she move to America?

_____

5 Who did she live with?

_____

6 How did Priscilla meet Mike Stone?

_____

7 Did Elvis and Priscilla get on well after they got divorced?

_____

C Read the audio script on page 77 to check your answers.

WRITING linking words

7 Correct the linking words in the sentences.

1 I didn't like the film ~~so~~ *because* it was scary.

2 We saw Pompeii *but* we thought it was wonderful.

3 She didn't like her job *because* she decided to leave.

4 They couldn't get married *and* her father wouldn't allow it.

5 He started taekwondo lessons *but* he wanted to get fit.

6 They wanted to buy the house *so* the bank didn't give them the money.

7 I bought a new computer *because* I'm having lots of problems with it.

8 I didn't sleep very well *but* I'm very tired today.

VOCABULARY conversation topics

1 Label pictures 1–8 with the words and phrases in the box below.

> your work/studies   films   your health problems
> your last holiday   your new computer   your family
> the weather   politics   sport

1 _____

2 _____

3 _____

4 _____

5 _____

6 _____

7 _____

8 _____

FUNCTION making conversation

2 Complete the conversations with the words and phrases in the box.

> do you   work here   in touch   did you   you know
> my friend   isn't it   meet you   would you
> good weekend

1 A: Hello, Helen. This is _____ Joshua.
   B: Hi, Joshua. Pleased to meet you.
2 A: Did you have a _____?
   B: Yes, thanks. I didn't do much.
3 A: Nice day, _____?
   B: Yes, it's lovely.
4 A: So, do you _____?
   B: No, I'm just visiting.
5 A: _____ like a drink?
   B: Thanks. I'd love a glass of water.
6 A: _____ watch the film last night?
   B: Yes. It was brilliant.
7 A: So, what _____ do?
   B: I'm a nurse.
8 A: How do _____ Raffa?
   B: We were students together.
9 A: It was nice to _____.
   B: Yes, see you again soon.
10 A: I hope we meet again soon.
   B: Yes, let's keep _____.

LEARN TO sound natural

3 ▶1.3 Listen and mark the linked words.
1 Do you like it here?
2 Where are you going?
3 I come from Italy.
4 It's a beautiful day.
5 I'm afraid I can't remember.
6 Where did you buy it?
7 I'm sorry, but I don't understand.

4 ▶1.4 Listen and write down what you hear.
1 _____
2 _____
3 _____
4 _____
5 _____
6 _____

VOCABULARY work

1 Use the clues to complete the word puzzle.

1 a business that makes or sells things or provides services
2 a person you work with
3 everyone who works in a company
4 a job you have to do
5 a person who manages the workers
6 someone who works for a business
7 a place where many people work at desks
8 money you get regularly when you do a job

²C O L L E A G U E

GRAMMAR present simple and continuous

2 Match a)–b) with i)–ii).

1 a) I'm doing my homework _____
   b) I do my homework _____
   i) on the bus most days.
   ii) so I can't come to the party with you.

2 a) I'm not enjoying this film. _____
   b) I don't enjoy films. _____
   i) Can we watch the other DVD?
   ii) I prefer reading.

3 a) I'm looking for _____
   b) I look for _____
   i) new artists. It's an interesting job.
   ii) Maria. Have you seen her?

4 a) I'm standing _____
   b) I stand _____
   i) on the bridge every day and watch the boats.
   ii) on the bridge. I can see you!

5 a) The train is arriving _____
   b) The train arrives _____
   i) late sometimes.
   ii) in London now. See you in five minutes.

6 a) Are you using _____
   b) Do you use _____
   i) this pen? No? OK, I'll use it for a moment.
   ii) a pen and paper or do you do everything on the computer?

3 Complete the conversations with the present simple or the present continuous.

1 A: Why _____ (you / smile)?
   B: Ahmed just told me a very funny joke!

2 A: How many people _____ (you / know) here?
   B: No one except you!

3 A: Did you hear that noise next door?
   B: Yes! What _____ (they / do)?

4 A: What _____ (you / drink)?
   B: Apple juice. But I don't want any more, thanks.

5 A: _____ (he / be) an actor?
   B: No, that's his famous twin brother.

6 A: Which one is Sharon?
   B: _____ (she / wear) the blue Gucci dress.

4A Complete the text with the present simple or the present continuous.

Here are some photos of my new friends. This is Amei. She ¹_____ (be) an artist, but at the moment she ²_____ (work) as a teacher. She ³_____ (not like) teaching very much! And this is Bruce, her husband. This is Hernan. He's from Santiago, Chile. He ⁴_____ (be) a maths teacher, but he ⁵_____ (do) his Master's in education in the USA at the moment. In the photo he ⁶_____ (smile) because he passed an exam that day!

This is Julio from Colombia. He ⁷_____ (have) a job in an oil company. In the picture he ⁸_____ (play) his guitar – he's really good! The other picture is Natasha from Trinidad. She graduated last year and she ⁹_____ (look) for a job. Her parents ¹⁰_____ (visit) her at the moment.

B Read the text again and label the people in the pictures.

1 _____

2 _____

3 _____

4 _____

5 _____

READING

5A Read the text and choose the best summary.

1 How one company keeps its workers happy.

2 Things that companies do to motivate their workers.

3 Working for the world's best companies.

HAPPY CO.

Are they great ideas or just crazy? Here are some ways that companies keep their employees happy.

1 Sport can be a good way for busy workers to relax. Parette Somjen Architects, New Jersey, has a small golf course in the office. The first part of the course is on the third floor. When your ball drops down the ninth hole, the course continues on the second floor. An even more relaxing sport is fishing. Maybe this is why a company called Sheboyan keeps a pond full of fish. The employees go fishing after work and keep the fish that they catch.

2 What about alternatives to boring suits and company uniforms? One company has 'fancy-dress Fridays'. On the last Friday of every month, each department chooses a theme and the workers dress up accordingly. One department came as superheroes, with the boss dressed as Batman. Another department chose 'monsters'; there were three Frankensteins and two King Kongs! And how about this idea from a company called 09Octane, in Denver, USA: they hold moustache-growing competitions for employees and customers! For men only, of course!

3 Some companies like to take their employees out of the office. Brogan and Partners takes its workers on a trip every year. The workers go to the airport, but they don't know what country they are flying to! Trips in the past have included Amsterdam, Iceland and the Caribbean. In another company, Innocent Smoothies, the staff go on free snowboarding holidays. And if workers stay with the USA-based New Belgium Brewing Company for five years, they get a free trip to Belgium to taste beer.

B Read the text again and answer the questions.

1 Where exactly is the golf course at Parette Somjen Architects?

_____

2 How can the employees at Sheboyan relax after work?

_____

3 What are 'fancy-dress Fridays'?

_____

4 What surprise do the employees of Brogan and Partners get every year?

_____

C Find words in the text to match definitions 1–6.

1 a small area of water (paragraph 1)

_____

2 other possibilities (paragraph 2)

_____

3 clothes that everyone in a company or a group wears (paragraph 2)

_____

4 party clothes that make you look like a famous character or person from a story (2 words, paragraph 2)

_____ _____

5 large, ugly frightening creatures (paragraph 2)

_____

6 a visit to a place (paragraph 3)

_____

WRITING an email

6A Underline the correct alternative.

[1]*Dear/Hi* Mr Yevgeny,

I am writing [2]*about/for* the advertisement for a hotel cleaner that I saw in *Jobs Monthly*. I have attached my CV.

I look forward to [3]*hear/hearing* from you.

[4]*Yours sincerely/Bye for now*,

Milly Clapton

---

[5]*Bye/Hi* Dave,

[6]*It's/There's* about the party. Can you bring your CD player and some CDs?

[7]*See/Speak* you soon.

[8]*Yours sincerely/Cheers*,

Elena

B Your company has decided to have 'fancy-dress Fridays'. Write a formal email to your colleagues (50–100 words). Include the information below.

1 Say what you are writing about.

2 Explain what 'fancy-dress Fridays' are.

3 Invite ideas for fancy dress.

VOCABULARY jobs

1 Match the jobs in the box with what the people say.

motorcycle courier   sales rep   fashion designer
foreign correspondent   personal trainer
IT consultant   rescue worker

1 The biggest problem in my job is the number of cars in the city. _motorcycle courier_

2 I like my job because I travel the world and see important events. _____

3 We believe in making clothes for normal people, not only beautiful models. _____

4 In my job, you need to love computers and technology. _____

5 In my team, we save about ten lives a year. _____

6 My job is easier when I like the product that I'm trying to sell. _____

7 I like helping people to get stronger and fitter. _____

2A Look at the jobs in Exercise 1 again. How many syllables does each job have? Write the job next to the number of syllables.

7 syllables: _motorcycle courier_

6 syllables: _____

5 syllables: (3 jobs) _____ _____
_____

4 syllables: _____

2 syllables: _____

B Underline the stressed syllables.

C ▶ 2.1 **Listen and check.**

VOCABULARY work collocations

3 Complete the job advertisements with the words in the box below.

deal   team   holidays   salary   with   pressure   risk

IT CONSULTANT needed for six-month contract in Abu Dhabi. You will need to 1 _deal_ with IT problems in the head office at Magran James Manufacturers. You must be good at working in a 2_____ and working under 3_____

Benefits: very good 4_____ ($240,000 tax-free) and excellent conditions. House provided.

If you want a job with long 5_____, come and speak to Safari Travel Inc. We are looking for qualified safari guides. You don't need to 6_____ your life fighting lions and crocodiles, but you must know about outdoor living and be good at dealing 7_____ customers. Call the number below for more information.

0802 276 6671

GRAMMAR adverbs of frequency

4A Underline the best alternative to complete the quotes.

1 'People who work sitting down *always/never* get paid more than people who work standing up.'

2 'The successful people are *occasionally/usually* the ones who listen more than they talk.'

3 'Politicians *always/never* believe what they say so they are surprised when other people do.'

4 '*Once in a while/Usually* teachers will open a door, if you're lucky, but you have to enter alone.'

5 'Great artists like Van Gogh *rarely/sometimes* live to see their success.'

6 'Doctors are the same as lawyers. The only difference is that lawyers rob you, but doctors rob you **and** kill you *occasionally/usually*.'

7 'Find something you love doing, and you'll *sometimes/never* have to work a day in your life.'

8 'The only place where success *hardly ever/always* comes before work is in the dictionary.'

B ▶ 2.2 **Listen and check.**

5A Complete the sentences with one of the adverbs in the box and *happen*.

hardly ever   never   rarely   often

1 'My job is really safe. In twenty years, I've only heard of one accident.' (estate agent)
Accidents _hardly ever happen_.

2 'Bad accidents happen once every two or three years.' (plumber)
Accidents _____.

3 'It's a very dangerous job. A lot of people die.' (fisherman)
Accidents _____.

4 'We have a completely safe job. The only danger is to your eyes from reading too much!' (university lecturer)
Accidents _____.

B Now do the same for these sentences.

once in a while   occasionally   always

1 'In ten years I've heard about one or two accidents when animals have attacked.' (vet)
Accidents _____.

2 'Danger is part of the job. When you work with guns, accidents happen every day.' (soldier)
Accidents _____.

3 'Three or four times a year there are serious accidents.' (electrician)
Accidents _____.

LISTENING

6A Label the picture with the words in the box.

~~safari guide~~   tour bus   tourists   male elephant   pool

2 _____

1 _Safari guide_

3 _____

4 _____

5 _____

B ▶ 2.3 Listen to two people talking about what happened in the picture. Answer the questions.

1 Who is speaking in each story?

_____

2 Why was it a frightening experience?

_____

3 What happened in the end? Was anyone injured?

_____

C Read the sentences. Are they from Story 1 or Story 2? Listen again and check.

1 I had a bus full of tourists. There were fifteen of them. _Story 1_

2 There were twenty of us tourists. _Story 2_

3 It was a beautiful, clear evening, and about seven o'clock we saw some elephants. _____

4 One evening, at about six o'clock, we went for a drive in the tour bus. _____

5 I told the tourists to walk very slowly back to the bus. _____

6 [He] told us to run back to the bus as fast as possible. _____

D Circle the correct meaning for the phrases in bold, a) or b).

1 They could **get off the bus**.
   a) stay on the bus
   b) leave the bus

2 The elephant **charged** at us.
   a) ran at us very fast
   b) made a loud noise

3 The tourists were **screaming**.
   a) making a loud noise because they were frightened
   b) getting angry

4 I started driving **as fast as possible**.
   a) not very quickly
   b) very quickly

E Read the audio script on page 77 and check your answers.

FUNCTION expressing likes/dislikes

1A Complete the sentences with the words in the box.

don't	on	absolutely	can't	very	love	mind	keen

1 I'm very _____ on cooking and I _____ love great food.

2 I _____ riding my motorbike. I _____ stand sitting in an office all day.

3 I'm quite keen _____ technology and I don't _____ dealing with other people's computer problems.

4 I'm _____ keen on working with money and I _____ like people wasting it on stupid things.

B ▶ 2.4 Listen and check.

C Match 1–4 above with the jobs below.

accountant _____   IT consultant _____

chef _____   motorcycle courier _____

2A Put the words in the correct order to make sentences.

1 like / team / you / a / do / in / working ?

_____

2 working / can't / pressure / I / stand / under

_____

3 my / not / I'm / very / on / boss / keen

_____

4 colleagues / don't / my / like / I

_____

5 dealing / don't / customers / I / mind / with

_____

6 keen / sport / you / on / are ?

_____

B Match sentences 1–6 in Exercise 2A with responses a)–f) below.

a) Why? What's wrong with her? _____

b) I'm not surprised. They don't seem very friendly. _____

c) That's good because it's important for a sales assistant. _____

d) I love it, especially football. _____

e) Why? Do you get stressed? _____

f) Yes, I do. Actually, I hate working alone. _____

VOCABULARY types of work

3 Match the types of work below to sentences 1–8.

~~works in accounts~~   **works in retail**

works in education   works in sales and marketing

works in the fashion industry

works in the entertainment industry

works in the tourist industry

works in the food industry

1 I deal with the money that goes in and out of the company. _works in accounts_

2 I prepare fresh sandwiches for our customers. _____

3 I design clothes. _____

4 I teach teenagers maths and science. _____

5 I organise advertising for the company's products and speak to customers. _____

6 I show people all the best places to visit and things to do in my city. _____

7 I act in films and in the theatre. _____

8 I work in a shop, selling products to our customers. _____

LEARN TO respond and ask more questions

4A Complete the words in the conversations.

Conversation 1

A: On Saturday I went to a conference about the z-phone, this amazing new technology.

B: Th__t s__nds __nt__r__st__ng.

A: Well, everybody's talking about it.

B: So h__w d____s it w__rk?

A: Oh, I don't know. I didn't go to the presentations. I only went for the free food.

Conversation 2

A: Today I was offered a job as a babysitter.

B: Th__t's gr____t!

A: Not really. They only offered me five euros an hour.

B: Oh, I s____. So did you accept the job?

A: No. I'm going to look for something better.

B: R__ght. What did you tell them?

A: I said, 'Dad, I know the baby is my sister, but I want a better salary!'

B ▶ 2.5 Listen and check.

C ▶ 2.6 Listen and say B's part. Focus on the intonation for sounding interested.

3.1 | TIME OUT

VOCABULARY time out

1 Complete the sentences with a suitable verb.

1 I'm going to ___see___ a jazz band tonight. My sister says they're really good.

2 I usually _____ the bus to work because it's easy and it's cheap.

3 We like to _____ to a museum at the weekend. You can learn new things, and it's better than watching television.

4 Did you _____ the photographic exhibition in the Sainsbury Centre? It was brilliant.

5 I'm really hungry. Can we stop and _____ a snack from this café?

6 We're going to _____ a drink in the bar later. Do you want to meet us there?

7 I really want to _____ dancing. I haven't been for ages!

8 Why don't we _____ sightseeing? We can spend the whole day walking around the city.

9 Where do you want to _____ dinner? There's a nice restaurant around the corner.

GRAMMAR present continuous/*be going to* for future

2A Put the words in the correct order to make questions.

1 going / holiday / are / you / away / year / this / on ?
_____

2 is / dinner / evening / who / your / cooking / this ?
_____

3 are / going / to / dentist / when / the / you ?
_____

4 weekend / are / this / doing / you / what ?
_____

5 play / are / sport / you / to / this / any / going / week ?
_____

6 you / marry / are / to / going / Roberto ?
_____

7 what / meeting / you / time / your / are / sister ?
_____

8 are / to / English / do / your / what / improve / going / you / to ?
_____

9 you / a / the / are / party / at / weekend / having ?
_____

10 gym / work / are / to / the / you / after / going ?
_____

B Match questions 1–10 with answers a)–j).

a) Nobody. I'm just going to eat some salad and fruit.

b) Six o'clock. We're going out for a meal.

c) Yes, we're getting married in the summer.

d) I'm going to read as much as possible in English.

e) Next Tuesday – in the morning.

f) No. I'm going to Greece next summer, but I'm not going anywhere this year.

g) Yes, I'm playing tennis with Jim on Friday.

h) Some friends are coming to stay, so we're taking them up to the mountains.

i) No, I'm going out for dinner.

j) Yes, do you want to come?

3 Complete the conversations with the phrases in the box below.

> are you coming going to look are you going
> 'm speaking are you doing 're going are meeting
> 'm staying

1 A: Hi, Boris. What _____ later?
   B: Nothing much. I _____ at home tonight.

2 A: What are your plans for the summer?
   B: I'm _____ for a job.

3 A: Have you seen Anita?
   B: No, but I _____ to her later.

4 A: When does your brother arrive?
   B: My parents _____ him at the station at 6.30p.m.

5 A: _____ to the party on Saturday?
   B: I'm not sure. I haven't been invited.

6 A: Where _____ for your holiday?
   B: We _____ cycling in the Netherlands.

THREE THINGS TO DO IN ... LONDON

There are so many things to see and do in London, sometimes it's difficult to know where to start. In this week's guide, we look at three things you can't miss when you visit London.

Go to the National Gallery in Trafalgar Square. Here you can see some of the most famous paintings and drawings in the world. There's Leonardo da Vinci's *The Virgin Of The Rocks*, Monet's *The Water-Lily Pond*, and Van Gogh's *Sunflowers*. And there's a whole room dedicated to the works of Rembrandt. There are around 2,200 paintings in the collection, with 1,000 permanently on display in the main galleries. And to make things even better, most of the exhibitions are free.

They say that Paris has the Eiffel Tower, New York has the Empire State Building, and London has the London Eye. This is one of the biggest observation wheels in the world and it takes you up to 135 metres. The London Eye is on the River Thames, opposite the Houses of Parliament and

Westminster Abbey. When you go up, you can see many of London's best sights and have a fantastic view of the city. One thing to remember though: try to choose a day when it's not raining, or you won't see very much at all!

Hyde Park is one of the largest parks in London. With over 4,000 trees and lots of different types of birds and butterflies, it's easy to forget you're in a big city. Play tennis, take a boat out on the Serpentine Lake or go for a swim. There's an art gallery and there are four cafés and restaurants. Great concerts take place in Hyde Park too – Nelson Mandela celebrated his ninetieth birthday with a concert in the park. In the past, there have also been important protests here. More than two million people joined the Stop the War protest in Hyde Park in 2003. So, come and see for yourself: Hyde Park has something for everyone.

READING

4A Read the article and complete sentences 1–8 with a name or a number.

1 In the National Gallery you can see a famous painting of some flowers by _____.

2 One painter has a room with only his paintings in it. His name is _____.

3 The National Gallery has _____ paintings altogether.

4 The London Eye is a big observation wheel on the River _____.

5 It is _____ metres tall.

6 There are more than _____ trees in Hyde Park.

7 The lake in the middle of Hyde Park is called the _____.

8 There was a big concert in Hyde Park to celebrate Nelson Mandela's birthday when he was _____ years old.

B Read the article again and answer the questions.

1 How much do you have to pay to visit many of the exhibitions in the National Gallery?

_____

2 What do people like to visit when they go to Paris and New York?

_____

3 What is special about the views from the London Eye?

_____

4 Why is it important to have good weather when you visit the London Eye?

_____

5 Why is it 'easy to forget you're in a big city' when you visit Hyde Park?

_____

6 What different activities can you do in Hyde Park?

_____

7 Why did two million people go to Hyde Park in 2003?

_____

WRITING invitations

5 Find and correct the mistakes. There are eight grammatical mistakes in the emails. The first one has been done for you.

Hi Mike,
I'm playing
~~I play~~ football later with a few of the boys from work. Would you like to coming?
Dan

Dan,
I'm sorry, but I busy tonight. I take Leila out for a meal. Wish me luck! Thanks anyway.
Mike

Hi guys,
A few of us is going out for a curry on Friday night. Do you want come with us? We're meet at the Indian Tree at 8p.m.
Emma

Hi Emma,
I love to. See you there.
Jan

6A Complete the email invitations using the prompts.

1_____ (I / have / party) at my house on Saturday.
2_____ (you / want / come)?
3_____ (we / go / have / music) and plenty of food. Bring your friends too. Just let me know.
Kristoph

4_____ (Julie / get / tickets / go / theatre) next Wednesday.
5_____ (we go / see / Shakespeare play) – I can't remember which one. 6_____ (would / like / come)? The tickets are £17.50.
Becca

B Write your own answers to the emails explaining why you would like to/can't come. Write 50–100 words.

VOCABULARY the arts

1 Complete the words in the reviews.

> **MARK ROTHKO AT THE MODERN ART MUSEUM**
>
> If you want to see a modern American master, do not miss this ¹__xh__b__t__ __n of Rothko ²p__ __nt__ngs at one of the world's finest ³__rt g__ll__r__ __s, M.A.M. Many of the later works of this magnificent ⁴p__ __nt__r are collected here, and they show the ⁵__rt__st at his best.

> **SONGS FOR FREEDOM – DIVERSE ARTISTS AT PEDDLERS' FIELD**
>
> At this outdoor ⁶c__nc__rt we heard the best of British ⁷r__ck, ⁸p__p and ⁹j__zz as twelve ¹⁰b__nds played for twenty minutes each to raise money for political prisoners. The ¹¹__ __d__ __nc__ simply loved the ¹²p__rf__rm__nc__s.

2 Cross out the word which is not possible in each sentence.

1 I went to a *jazz/rock/~~band~~* concert.
2 He is one of the greatest *painters/sculptures/songwriters* of the twentieth century.
3 We went to the theatre and saw a great *performance/concert hall/play*.
4 We saw a wonderful *exhibition/performance/art gallery* of her work.
5 I love *concert/pop/classical* music.
6 I spent some time talking to the *audience/play/artist* afterwards.
7 I just bought a very unusual *painting/sculpture/jazz*.
8 Lots of famous *singers/actors/paintings* live in Los Angeles.
9 We walked around the *art gallery/play/exhibition*.
10 She's a very talented *composer/songwriter/sculpture*.

3A Complete the sentences with a word that matches the stress pattern.

1 Rembrandt is my favourite *painter*. Oo
2 I couldn't see the band at all because I was at the back of the _____ hall. Oo
3 Most of Van Gogh's _____ are worth millions. Oo
4 I like Beethoven, but Mozart is my favourite _____. oOo
5 I don't really like _____ music. I prefer more modern styles. Ooo
6 Rodin is my favourite _____. I love his sculpture *The Thinker*. Oo
7 Kanye West is a really great _____. His words and music are always excellent. Ooo
8 We saw an _____ of Cindy Sherman's photos. I can't remember the name of the gallery. ooOo
9 The _____ in Rio de Janeiro was U2's greatest. Millions of people saw it. oOo

B Check your answers. The answers are in the box in the wrong order.

> classical exhibition composer performance
> sculptor songwriter paintings concert

C ▶ 3.1 Listen and repeat.

LISTENING

4A Look at the picture. What do you think the other man says?

What do you think, Terry?

B ▶ 3.2 Listen to the conversation and answer the questions.

1 What does Terry think of the painting? _____
2 Was it expensive or cheap? _____
3 Who do you think Mary is? _____

C Listen again. What are the answers to Terry's questions?

1 How much did the painting cost? _____
2 Has Mary seen the painting? _____
3 Does Mary like modern art? _____

GRAMMAR questions without auxiliaries

5A Complete the questions with the pairs of words in the box.

Who invented	Who earned
Who wrote	Whose album
Which composer	Which painting
Which French	What happens
What country	What film	Whose life

1 _____ _____ makes the most films every year?

2 _____ _____ lost his hearing?

3 _____ _____ by Van Gogh cost more: *Sunflowers* or *Portrait of Dr Gachet*?

4 _____ _____ the dance called salsa?

5 _____ _____ museum appears in the novel *The Da Vinci Code*?

6 _____ _____ to the heroes at the end of Shakespeare's *Romeo and Juliet*?

7 _____ _____ the songs *Yellow*, *Clocks* and *Viva la Vida*?

8 _____ _____ won eleven Oscars in 2003?

9 _____ _____ $225 million in 2005 for her TV show?

10 _____ _____ became the biggest selling record in history?

11 _____ _____ changes when he finds a golden ticket in a Wonka bar of chocolate?

B Match questions 1–11 with answers a)–k).

a) the Louvre

b) *The Return of the King* (part 3 of *The Lord of the Rings*)

c) *Portrait of Dr Gachet*

d) African slaves in the Caribbean, though the modern version comes from Cuba

e) Coldplay

f) Oprah Winfrey

g) Ludwig van Beethoven

h) they both die

i) India

j) Charlie's (in the novel and film *Charlie and the Chocolate Factory*)

k) Michael Jackson's (the album is *Thriller*)

6 Write questions for the underlined answers. Start your questions with *Who*, *What (music)* or *Whose*.

1 *Who made drum and bass music popular in the 1990s* ?

Goldie made drum and bass music popular in the 1990s.

2 _____ ?

The blues was invented by African Americans in the USA.

3 _____ ?

African Americans from the South brought the blues to the north in the early twentieth century.

4 _____ ?

George Johnson's song *Laughing Song* (1895) was the first blues recording.

5 _____ ?

Fela Kuti's nightclub played Afrobeat for many years.

6 _____ ?

Farmers first played bhangra music to celebrate the spring.

7 _____ ?

Jazzy Bains' album, *Folk and Funky* (1995), made bhangra music popular in the West.

8 _____ ?

Afrobeat music mixes traditional Nigerian music with jazz and funk.

9 _____ ?

Fela Kuti made Afrobeat famous.

10 _____ ?

Bhangra music, originally from the Punjab region in India, has become world-famous.

Bhangra

VOCABULARY collocations

1A Find six more verbs in the word square.

A	R	R	A	N	G	E	V
C	A	N	C	E	L	M	O
H	B	Y	H	A	V	E	D
A	O	E	E	I	G	P	I
N	O	S	C	L	F	N	T
G	K	T	K	P	E	L	A
E	R	O	O	C	T	K	L
T	M	F	A	E	S	R	K

(arrange circled in top row)

B There is a verb missing in each sentence. Complete the sentences with verbs from the word square.

arrange
1 Did you /to meet friends? If you didn't, we can meet later.

2 She called me because she wanted to a chat.

3 Please a table for us at the Blue Fin Restaurant tonight.

4 There's been a problem and I can't attend, so I'm calling to my reservation.

5 I'd like to some information: what time is the last train to Bern?

6 I'd like to come to the 4.30 performance, not the 6.30 one, and I'm calling to my ticket.

7 The manager of Triad Books is on the phone. He wants to business.

FUNCTION making a phone call

2 Match sentence beginnings 1–7 with endings a)–g).

1	Who's	a)	calling.
2	Hello, this	b)	to call you back.
3	Can I speak	c)	leave a message?
4	Can I	d)	is John.
5	I'm afraid she's	e)	calling?
6	I'll ask her	f)	not here at the moment.
7	Thanks for	g)	to Alexandra, please?

3 Find and correct the mistakes. There are four mistakes in the conversation.

A: Hello. I'm Jim. Is Trudy there?

B: I'm afraid but she's not here at the moment.

A: Oh, really? Can I leave the message?

B: Of course.

A: Can you tell her that we need to discuss the party on Friday?

B: Yes, I will. I'll ask her for calling you back.

A: Thanks a lot.

B: You're welcome. Bye.

A: Bye.

4 Number the sentences from the phone conversation in the correct order, 1–10.

a) Yes. I'm going to be twenty minutes late. _____

b) Thank you very much. See you soon. _____

c) One moment. Who's calling, please? _____

d) Hello. Can I speak to Kim? _____

e) Thanks for calling. Bye. _____

f) Good morning. Craven Beauty Parlour. Beverley speaking. _____

g) No problem. I'll tell her. _____

h) It's Liz Holder here. _____

i) Hi, Liz. Oh, I'm afraid Kim's at lunch. Is it about today's appointment? _____

j) Bye. _10_

LEARN TO manage phone problems

5 Put the words in the correct order to complete the questions.

1 A: Hi, I'm waiting for a delivery of fifteen chocolate rabbits. Have you sent them yet?

 B: One moment. _____? (check / just / I / can)

2 A: Hello, this is Hillary Kenton, calling from Newark.

 B: Sorry, _____. (catch / that / didn't / I) Did you say Hillary Clinton from New York?

3 A: Hello, my name is Aloysius Venoziak Frobisher Menkovsky.

 B: _____? (repeat / you / can / that)

4 A: Hi, um ... I'm ... um ... waiting for a ... er ... a package from Dublin.

 B: Sorry, _____? (speak / you / up / can / please)

5 A: Hello. I'd like to order two Pentium Bidmark 6.40 large photocopiers, three Ribdale Energy Star fax machines, five Rubicon Jump Drives, and ...

 B: Sorry, _____? (down / slow / you / can / please)

LISTENING

6 ▶ 3.3 Listen to three phone conversations and complete the notes.

1 Pauline calling. No _____ for the concert. Call back tonight _____.

2 Elise called. Meet her at the _____ at _____.

3 Roundhouse Bar and Grill doesn't take _____. Come before _____.

GRAMMAR question forms

1A Complete questions 1–9 with a question word or an auxiliary verb.

1 When _does_ the film start?

2 _____ often do you see your grandmother?

3 _____ are my keys? I can't find them.

4 _____ you enjoy watching films?

5 Who _____ he live with?

6 _____ you know Sabina? She's my best friend.

7 _____ do you usually go on holiday?

8 _____ many hours do you work?

9 _____ time did you get here? I'm sorry I'm late.

B Match questions 1–9 with answers a)–i).

a) About five minutes ago. Don't worry, it's no problem.

b) No, I don't. Hi, Sabina.

c) Once or twice a year.

d) We usually go to Spain. My aunt has a house there.

e) Here they are. They were on the television!

f) He lives with his brother and another student.

g) Yes, I do. But I don't like horror films.

h) Usually about thirty-five hours a week.

i) In half an hour.

VOCABULARY phrases with *get, go, have, spend*

2A Put the phrases in the box into the correct column in the table below.

married   children   dancing   money on clothes
time off work   the bus   time with someone   on well
a barbecue   on holiday   to the cinema
dinner with someone   sightseeing

get	go	have	spend
married			

B Which phrases would you use for situations 1–9?

1 You meet someone you like and want to spend your life together. _get married_

2 You travel home on public transport. _____

3 You visit your mother every day. _____

4 You often go to discos or clubs because you like doing this. _____

5 You do this to watch a film. _____

6 You eat in the garden and the food is cooked over a fire. _____

7 You have a good relationship with someone. _____

8 You visit the places tourists see in a city. _____

9 You eat a meal in the evening with a friend. _____

GRAMMAR past simple: regular/irregular

3 Put the verbs in brackets into the past simple.

ANGRY MOTHER PUNISHES SIXTY-ONE-YEAR-OLD SON

AN ANGRY MOTHER [1]_____ (take) the house keys and money away from her sixty-one-year-old son, because he [2]_____ (stay) out late at night, and [3]_____ (not / tell) her where he planned to go when he [4]_____ (go) out. The mother, who is eighty-one years old, even went to the police in Caltagione, Italy, the town where she lives. She [5]_____ (ask) the police to tell her son that he should 'grow up' and behave in a better way towards his mother.

The son [6]_____ (complain) that it was his mother who was the problem. He [7]_____ (say) that he [8]_____ (not / get) enough money every week, and that his mother [9]_____ (not / cook) well. 'It's not my fault,' he [10]_____ (tell) reporters. 'She always treats me badly. And her cooking is really awful!'

A police officer [11]_____ (talk) to the mother and the son, and they finally [12]_____ (decide) to go home together.

FUNCTION making conversation

4A Complete the words in the conversations.

1 A: Hello. My name's Felipe. It's n_i_c_e_ to meet you.

B: Hi, I'm Magda. Nice to meet you t___.

2 A: It's a lovely day, i___t it?

B: Yes, the weather's beaut__f__l.

3 A: S__, where exactly do you c__m_ from?

B: Zaragoza. It's a small c__ty in Northern Spain.

4 A: Did you have a g___d w___k___d?

B: Yes, I had a lovely t__m__, thank you.

5 A: So, w_____d you l__k_ a dr___k?

B: Yes, I'd l__v_ a glass of w__t__r.

6 A: It was n__c__ to m___t you, Magda.

B: Yes, let's try to k___p in t___ch.

B ▶ RC1.1 Listen and check.

GRAMMAR present simple and present continuous

5 Find and correct the mistakes. There is a mistake in each of the sentences.

1 I ~~am not liking~~ _don't like_ fish.

2 I stay with some friends for a few days so I can look for somewhere to live.

3 I'm not knowing what time the lesson starts.

4 They spend time with their family in Germany at the moment.

5 We're usually going out for a pizza about once a week.

6 I'm not understanding where Jazz is. He never arrives late.

7 Do you watch this programme? Or can I watch the football on the other channel?

GRAMMAR adverbs of frequency

6 The adverbs of frequency are in the wrong place in each sentence. Correct the sentences.

1 We come always here. It's the best club in the area.
2 Hardly ever I see her because she works for a different company.
3 My occasionally parents help us when we're busy.
4 I get up at usually about 6.30a.m.
5 Sal's very upset and says she wants to see him never again.
6 We go to once in a while Scotland.
7 Rarely I have the chance to spend time with my sister.
8 I take the children every day to school.

FUNCTION likes/dislikes

7 Complete each sentence so that it has the same meaning as the sentence above. Use the word(s) in brackets.

1 I don't enjoy getting up early.
   I *'m not very keen on* getting up early. (not very keen)
2 I like punk music very much.
   I _____ punk music. (absolutely)
3 I hate sales reps who try to sell me products on the telephone.
   I _____ sales reps who try to sell me products on the telephone. (stand)
4 Marjorie isn't very keen on doing housework.
   Marjorie _____ doing housework. (like)
5 I'm quite happy to do physical jobs.
   I _____ doing physical jobs. (mind)
6 John really doesn't like eating spicy food.
   John _____ eating spicy food. (hate)
7 I'm happy working in a team.
   I _____ in a team. (like)
8 I enjoy walking in the countryside.
   I _____ walking in the countryside. (keen)

GRAMMAR present continuous/*be going to* for future plans

8 Complete the sentences with the correct form of the verbs in brackets.

1 I _____ (go shopping) later. Do you want to come?
2 My sister _____ (have) a party on Friday, but I don't know what to wear.
3 He _____ (go) start karate lessons in January.
4 We _____ (stay) with my parents for the weekend.
5 _____ (you / come) to the lesson this evening? I'll see you there.
6 We _____ to Italy on the 19th December. (fly)

VOCABULARY work; the arts

9 Complete the words in sentences 1–8.

1 Pete gets a good s__l__ry, but he doesn't like his b__ss.
2 There were some wonderful p____nt__ngs in the exh__b__t____n.
3 We w__rk under a lot of pr__ss__re in the busy months.
4 There were hundreds of people from around the world in the a__d____nc__.
5 The best thing about the job is that I g__t very l__ng h__l__d__ys.
6 Leonard Cohen is not only a s__ng__r and a s__ngwr__t__r. He's also a musician and a poet – and he writes novels.
7 Neil Diamond was the __ct__r who played the J__zz Singer in the 1980 film.
8 I enjoy my job because I can always find an interesting t__sk to do.

GRAMMAR questions with/without auxiliaries

10A The auxiliary verb is missing in seven more of these questions. Add the missing auxiliary where necessary.

1 Who/your teacher? *is*
2 Where you come from?
3 Who forgot to bring the keys?
4 Why David leave his job?
5 How often you play football?
6 How much it cost to fly to Russia?
7 Which class won the competition?
8 Who wrote *The Jungle Book*?
9 When you last go to a concert?
10 Whose bag is that?
11 Why you learning English?
12 Where you buy that coat?

B Match questions 1–12 with answers a)–l).

a) Our class did. We won the competition!
b) About €300.
c) It's mine. Sorry, I left it there.
d) I come from Argentina.
e) I want to study in the USA.
f) Zavier. He always forgets things.
g) I play once or twice a week.
h) He didn't like his boss.
i) Two months ago. I saw a really good jazz trio.
j) Rudyard Kipling.
k) I bought it in Toronto last year.
l) Her name's Mrs Taylor.

TEST

Circle the correct option to complete the sentences.

1 What _____ the time?

a) be   b) is   c) are

2 When _____ start work?

a) do you   b) are you   c) you do

3 They _____ when they were on holiday and they fell in love.

a) have met   b) are meeting c) met

4 I _____ €100 on these boots and they're broken.

a) spend   b) spent   c) paid

5 Why _____ you sad? Is there a problem?

a) do   b) is   c) are

6 We always _____ about who does the shopping.

a) argue   b) get on   c) get to know

7 When _____ to the UK?

a) moved you b) did you move
c) did you moved

8 She _____ and walked away.

a) smile   b) smiled   c) smiles

9 When I _____ college, I started looking for a job.

a) leave   b) have left   c) left

10 Did you _____ a good weekend?

a) have   b) had   c) having

11 It was _____ you.

a) nice meet b) nice met   c) nice to meet

12 I usually _____ to Helen when I have a problem.

a) talking   b) talk   c) talked

13 We like to keep our prices low. This makes our _____ happy.

a) customers b) employee   c) staff

14 I'm looking for a job with a higher _____.

a) boss   b) salary   c) task

15 At the moment I _____ a book about a young boy in Afghanistan.

a) 'm reading b) read   c) going to read

16 I can't _____ computer games. I really hate them.

a) hate   b) stand   c) keen

17 It's important _____ good relationships with the other employees.

a) have   b) having   c) to have

18 I look forward to _____ from you.

a) hearing   b) heard   c) hear

19 It's a dangerous job: you _____ your life every day.

a) work   b) deal with   c) risk

20 We _____ a lot of different problems.

a) work   b) deal with   c) risk

21 I'm not very keen _____ violent films.

a) of   b) about   c) on

22 Eve _____ to Australia next month.

a) is going   b) went   c) go

23 I _____ dinner tonight. I'm just going to have a snack.

a) don't have b) 'm not having c) don't having

24 _____ to come out on Saturday night?

a) Do you like   b) Would you like
c) Are you liking

25 That _____ like a great idea.

a) is   b) seem   c) sounds

26 Bob Dylan is a brilliant _____.

a) songwriter b) band   c) performance

27 Mozart was a famous _____.

a) audience   b) classical   c) composer

28 Hi. _____ Petra speaking.

a) I am   b) This is   c) Here is

29 Sorry, I _____ that. Can you say it again?

a) did catch b) didn't caught c) didn't catch

30 What are your plans for the weekend? _____ anything nice?

a) Are you doing b) Did you do c) Do you do

TEST RESULT   **/30**

VOCABULARY *make and do*

1A Complete phrases 1–14 with *make* or *do*.

1 _____ a speech
2 _____ well
3 _____ a project
4 _____ some friends
5 _____ a phone call
6 _____ business
7 _____ a mistake
8 _____ something interesting
9 _____ a lot of sport
10 _____ a decision
11 _____ my homework
12 _____ an appointment
13 _____ my best
14 _____ a meal

B Write responses to questions 1–12 using a phrase with *make* or *do*. Use the past simple.

1 What did you do on your first day at your new school?
I made some friends.

2 How was the test?
I did my best.

3 How did you contact her?
_____

4 You were very fit and strong when you were younger, weren't you?
_____

5 Wasn't that the wrong address?
_____

6 I heard the restaurant was closed, so what did you do?
_____

7 What type of work did you do at school today?
_____

8 What did you do in the library after school?
_____

9 How did the Public Speaking conference finish?
_____

10 Did you arrange to see the doctor?
_____

11 What did you do in the city centre?
_____

12 How was the singing competition?
_____

GRAMMAR *present perfect + ever/never*

2 One sentence in each pair is correct. Circle the correct sentence, a) or b).

1 a) I've first played the guitar when I was a teenager.
  b) I first played the guitar when I was a teenager.

2 a) When you worked in Hollywood, have you ever met anyone famous?
  b) When you worked in Hollywood, did you ever meet anyone famous?

3 a) Have you ever eaten sushi? Try some!
  b) Did you ever eat sushi? Try some!

4 a) Last night I read until 2a.m.
  b) Last night I've read until 2a.m.

5 a) Did you ever see the film *No Country for Old Men*? I have the DVD.
  b) Have you ever seen the film *No Country for Old Men*? I have the DVD.

6 a) In 1989, the government did something that changed the world.
  b) In 1989, the government has done something that changed the world.

7 a) She has never been to the theatre.
  b) She has ever been to the theatre.

8 a) I've ever worked in retail in my life.
  b) I've never worked in retail in my life.

3 Read the letter and underline the correct alternative.

Hi Janine,

I ¹*was/have been* here for a week now, and already I ²*made/have made* lots of friends. I share a room with a man called Don. Yesterday he asked me, ³'*Did you ever spend/Have you ever spent* time in a place like this?' I told him I ⁴*went/have been* camping when I was ten. He ⁵*laughed/has laughed*! He ⁶*spent/has spent* half his life here!

There are lots of things to do: there's a gym, a cinema, a library and a few clubs. I ⁷*didn't have/haven't had* time to join any clubs yet, but this afternoon we ⁸*watched/have watched* a film in the cinema.

The only bad thing is the food. I ⁹*didn't ever eat/have never eaten* such terrible food before in my whole life!

Best wishes,

Bob

MORE THAN A HOBBY

Gordon Ramsay

Winston Churchill

Woody Allen

1 When Wallace Stevens walked into his office every morning, his colleagues didn't know about his secret. Stevens lived a double life. By day he worked for an insurance company. The rest of his life was spent becoming one of the greatest American poets of the twentieth century.

2 Secret talent is more common than we think, even with people who are already famous in one area. Take Luciano Pavarotti, one of the world's greatest classical singers. Not many people know that before he became a singer, he was an outstanding football player. The same is true of TV chef Gordon Ramsay, who is now well known for his brilliant cooking and his bad language. Ramsay played professional football for Rangers, one of Scotland's best teams.

3 A number of politicians first made their name in other jobs. Silvio Berlusconi, prime minister of Italy and a businessman, once sang professionally on cruise ships. Winston Churchill, prime minister of Great Britain, also had another talent: he wrote great history books. Churchill's books won him the Nobel Prize in Literature in 1953. Vaclav Havel, who was the first president of the Czech Republic, was also a great writer.

4 There are also musicians and actors who have secret talents. Paul McCartney and David Bowie are both painters, Paul Newman was a racing car driver, and actor Omar Sharif was one of the world's greatest card players. And only those who go to a little hotel bar in New York City every Monday would know that one of the best clarinet players in town is actor and film director Woody Allen. He certainly plays the clarinet better than Bill Clinton plays the saxophone.

4A Do you recognise any of the people in the photos? Why are they famous? What else are they good at? Read the text to find out.

B Read the text again. Are the statements true (T) or false (F)?

1 The people in the text are famous for one thing, but also good at another thing. ____

2 Wallace Stevens' colleagues didn't know he was a poet. ____

3 Gordon Ramsay was a chef before he became a famous footballer. ____

4 Berlusconi, Churchill and Havel were all writers and politicians. ____

5 Woody Allen plays the clarinet and the saxophone. ____

C Circle the correct meaning for the words and phrases from the text, a) or b).

1 lived a double life (paragraph 1)
   a) one person had two very different lifestyles
   b) a person had a difficult life

2 The same is true of (paragraph 2)
   a) this situation is very different from ...
   b) this situation is very similar to ...

3 bad language (paragraph 2)
   a) speaking badly about another person   b) saying bad words

4 made their name (paragraph 3)
   a) became famous   b) learnt to do something

correcting mistakes

5 Read the paragraph and find eight more mistakes (two grammar, three spelling, three punctuation).

THE GREATEST MIND IN FICTION

belong (gr)

Most of fiction's great minds belongs either to criminals or to the men and women who catch them. A greatest of these is probably Sherlock Holmes. The Holmes stories were written by Sir Arthur Conan Doyle a docter from edinburgh, Scotland. Conan Doyle knew a lot about the human body and pollice work, and he has used this information in his books. Very quickly, Conan Doyle's hero beccame popular. When Holmes was killed in one story, thousands of readers protested. Conan Doyle changed his mind, and Holmes appeared in another story

VOCABULARY education

1 Use the clues to complete the crossword.

¹M	A	K	E		²			³S		
I				⁴T	E	S	T	T		⁵L
S			⁶U					U		A
T			N					D		N
A		⁷P	I	A	N	O		Y		G
K			F							U
E			O							A
⁸S	⁹P	O	R	T						G
	L		¹⁰n							E
	A									S
	Y		¹¹							

Across

1 One of the best things about going to university is that you _make_ a lot of new friends.

4 On Friday, we have to do a _test_ so I need to learn the vocabulary.

7 I would love to play the _piano_, but our flat is too small to have one.

8 At my school we play a lot of _sport_. It keeps us fit.

10 I'm doing a course in computer skills, and most of the time I study _____.

11 I have to _____ an exam at the end of the year.

Down

1 I don't like speaking French because I make a lot of _mistakes_

2 At the end of the year, all the students give a _____.

3 When you _study_ art, you learn about painters like Picasso and Salvador Dali.

5 I'd like to study foreign _languages_ like Russian and Spanish.

6 At school we didn't have to wear a _uniform_. We wore our own clothes.

9 Every week we _play_ games like tennis or netball.

GRAMMAR can, have to

2 Read the advertisements and complete conversations 1 and 2 using can/can't/have to/don't have to.

LEARN TO PLAY MUSIC – BEGINNERS' CLASS

Saturday mornings 10–11a.m.   Fee: £40 for 6 lessons

Always wanted to play the drums? Or the guitar? Want to try the piano? Come and join us for fun music lessons. Try any instrument you want, and we'll help you learn to play. No previous experience necessary. We supply the instruments, so you don't need to bring your own.

Children and adults welcome.

Conversation 1

Susan: Hi. I'd like to come to the beginners' music class. Do I ¹_have to_ be able to play an instrument?

Teacher: No, you ²_____ play an instrument. You ³_____ choose your instrument here, and we'll help you to learn.

Susan: ⁴_____ I come to a lesson first to see if I like it?

Teacher: Well, I'm afraid you ⁵_____ come to the lessons unless you sign up for the whole course.

Susan: OK. ⁶_____ I bring children?

Teacher: Yes, you ⁷_____. Children love it.

Susan: Do I ⁸_____ bring my own instrument?

Teacher: No, we have instruments here you ⁹_____ use.

Conversation 2

JOIN OUR ARABIC LANGUAGE AND CULTURE COURSE

Tues/Thurs evenings 6–8p.m. Start date: 13th October

Full price: £180   Reduced rates for students: £130

Interested?

Just come along to the first class. No need to register first, just bring an enrolment form with you. Pay after the class if you wish to enrol.

Student: I'm a student. How much do I ¹_____ pay?

Secretary: It's a reduced rate, so you only ²_____ pay £130.

Student: Do I ³_____ register first?

Secretary: No, you ⁴_____ register. You ⁵_____ come along to the first class. If you like the class, you ⁶_____ complete the form at the end of the lesson.

Student: ⁷_____ I pay by cheque?

Secretary: Yes, you ⁸_____ pay by card or cheque on the night.

3A ▶ 4.1 Listen and complete the sentences.

1 How much _____ pay?

2 _____ park here?

3 _____ visit her before we leave.

4 _____ stay in this hotel.

5 _____ wear that!

6 _____ tell anyone.

B Practise saying the sentences.

GRAMMAR *can, have to, must*

4A Rewrite the sentences. Replace the underlined words with phrases with *can/can't*.

1 You <u>are not allowed to</u> have your mobile phone switched on.

_____

2 You have to register before <u>it's possible to</u> use the site.

_____

3 I'm afraid <u>it isn't possible for her to</u> speak to you at the moment.

_____

4 <u>It's OK to</u> use my computer if you want to.

_____

B Rewrite the sentences. Replace the underlined words with phrases with *have to/ don't have to/ must/ mustn't*. There may be more than one possible answer.

1 <u>It's necessary to</u> be good at foreign languages if you want to learn Mandarin.

_____

2 <u>It's important to</u> be there on time, or they won't let us in.

_____

3 <u>It isn't necessary for us to</u> have a licence to fish here.

_____

4 <u>It's important that you don't</u> tell him I'm here.

_____

5 Look at the rules and complete the conversation with *can/can't/have to/must/mustn't*. There may be more than one possible answer.

EXAM RULES

mobile phones	– no
talk to other students	– no
arrive on time	– yes
eat/drink in the examination room	– no (water – OK)
have a dictionary	– yes

Teacher: Are there any questions?

Dan: Yes. ¹*Can* we bring our mobile phones into the room?

Teacher: No, you ²_____. You ³_____ turn them off and leave them outside in your bag.

Julie: Is it OK to eat during the exam?

Teacher: No. You ⁴_____ have a bottle of water, but you ⁵_____ have anything else to eat or drink.

Marco: Do we ⁶_____ leave our dictionaries in our bags?

Teacher: No, you ⁷_____ bring dictionaries into the examination.

Dan: What happens if we arrive late?

Teacher: You ⁸_____ arrive on time, or you ⁹_____ come into the examination room.

Julie: ¹⁰_____ we talk to other students?

Teacher: No. You ¹¹_____ talk at all during the examination. Now, does everybody understand? Is everything clear?

LISTENING

6A ▶ 4.2 Listen to the first part of an interview about different types of learner. Match the type of learner with the pictures.

Picture: _____ – Holist, learns lots of information about a topic, but in no particular order

Picture: _____ – Serialist, learns things in sequence from the bottom up

B ▶ 4.3 Listen to the second part of the interview and mark each statement Serialist (S) or Holist (H).

1 This learner likes to understand detail. _____

2 This learner reads instructions before using a new piece of equipment. _____

3 This learner might read a chapter from the middle of a book first. _____

4 This learner makes a careful plan before writing. _____

5 This learner reads around the topic and makes lots of notes before writing. _____

C Circle the correct option, a) or b), to complete the statements.

1 Students
   a) are always either serialists or holists.
   b) often use both serialist and holist approaches.

2 Serialists like to learn things
   a) in the correct order.
   b) in any order.

3 A holist likes to have an idea of the 'big picture' and
   a) doesn't worry about detail.
   b) thinks that the detail is very important.

VOCABULARY language learning

1 Complete the words in the sentences.

1 I find remembering new words very difficult, so I try to m_____ise five to ten words a day. I write the word in a sentence and then say the sentence again and again in my head.

2 If I don't understand the meaning of a word, I l__k it u_ in a dictionary.

3 Sometimes I rer___d an article for a second time, looking for new words and phrases.

4 I like to ch___ on the internet. I speak to other learners from all over the world.

5 I like watching films in English, especially ones with su_____s.

6 It's a good idea to vi____ English web_____. You can do a lot of reading and listening.

FUNCTION giving advice

2 Read the website questions asking for advice. Put the words in the correct order to complete the answers.

I never have anything to talk about when I chat to friends on the internet.
1_____ (films / talking / try / about) you've seen recently.

I'm thinking about changing my hairstyle. Any ideas?
2_____ (think / don't / you / I / should) change it. It looks great.
3_____ (try / why / you / don't) red and black stripes? It's cool.

I really like my boss at work, and I want to ask him out on a date.
4_____ (good / I / it's / idea / think / a / don't) to ask your boss out. If it goes badly, you might lose your job!

I don't know what to buy my husband for his birthday. His only interest is watching sport.
5_____ (should / think / I / get / you) him a pair of trainers and tell him to do some sport instead of watching it all day!
6_____ (you / don't / why / buy) him some tickets to a football match?

I'm going to babysit for my nephews and nieces. They are six years old, three years old and eighteen months old. I've never done this before. Can anyone help?
7_____ (try / think / I / should / you) to make a simple recipe, like chocolate biscuits or a cake. They'll enjoy helping you.
8_____ (idea / it's / think / a / to / good) about the things you enjoyed doing as a child: colouring, making things, singing songs, etc.

3 Read the problems and complete the advice using the prompts in brackets.

I'm twenty-nine years old and I work in a bank. I love my job, I have good friends and a boyfriend who loves me. In many ways, my life is perfect, so I don't understand why I'm not happy. I'm always so stressed. I don't sleep well and now my bad moods are causing problems in our relationship. Why can't I just be happy?

1_____ sit down and work out what is making you feel unhappy. (think / should)

2_____ write a list of the things that you are happy about in your life, and a list of the things that are not right? (why / not)

3_____ try some natural remedies to help you sleep too. If you don't sleep, that will make you feel stressed. (good / idea)

4_____ about your problems with your boyfriend. Does he understand? (try / talk)

I have my end of university exams next month. I'm so frightened that I'm not going to pass them that I'm thinking of leaving the university, and not going to the exams. I have studied hard for three years, but now I feel like I don't know anything.

5_____ leave the university. If you've studied hard, you probably have nothing to worry about. (not / think / good / idea)

6_____ talking to your university professor. He/She can probably help? (why / you / try)

7_____ try some relaxation techniques to help you with the exam stress. (think / should)

8_____ go to the exams even if you feel like you won't pass them. You should at least try. Good luck! (good / idea)

LEARN TO respond to advice

4A Complete responses a)–f) with suitable words.

1 Why don't we go to the cinema tonight?
2 I don't think you should buy that car.
3 I think we should organise a party.
4 Maybe you should say sorry.
5 You shouldn't play so many computer games.
6 I think you should study more.

a) I _____ so. I'll call Louise later.
b) _____ right. I need to get out more.
c) That's _____ idea. Do you know what's on?
d) I suppose _____. I want to do well in the exam.
e) I'm not _____ a good idea. We're too busy.
f) You're _____. It's too expensive.

B Match the pieces of advice 1–6 with responses a)–f).

C ▶ 4.4 Listen and check.

D ▶ 4.5 Listen again to the advice. Say the response.

5.1 TRAVEL

VOCABULARY transport

1A Find fourteen types of transport in the word snake.

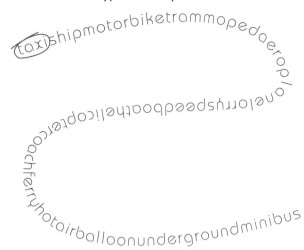

B Write the types of transport in the correct place in the word web.

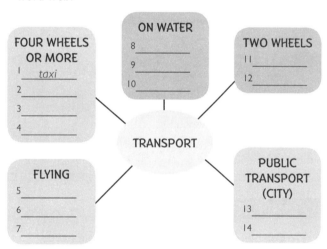

C What types of transport are they talking about?

1 'I always call one to get home at night.' _____

2 'I use it every morning to get to work. The roads are full of cars so it's the quickest way to travel.' _____

3 'It's my dream to travel in one of these, to feel the wind in my face and look down at the world below.' _____

4 'We enjoy touring foreign cities in them. They are perfect for groups of thirty or forty people.' _____

5 'I drive it for twelve hours a day. It's my job. I transport products for food companies across the country.' _____

6 'I can take you to your house. It's big enough for two people and I have two helmets.' _____

7 'It's the fastest way to travel on water. I use mine for waterskiing.' _____

8 'In the past, everyone used these to visit other continents. It took three weeks to get to the USA! Now this type of travel is only for rich people.' _____

GRAMMAR past simple and past continuous

2 Match sentence beginnings 1–8 with endings a)–h).

1 The last time they spoke to Marina
2 The teacher explained the exercise to us but
3 While I was shopping
4 It started to rain
5 My mobile phone rang while
6 I fell asleep while I
7 Were you doing something important
8 I didn't go out last night

a) while we were playing football.
b) when I phoned you?
c) were there any calls for me?
d) I was cooking.
e) because I was studying.
f) we weren't listening.
g) she was working in a bar.
h) was watching TV.

3 Complete the conversations with the past simple or the past continuous.

Conversation 1

A: I came to see you yesterday, but you weren't at home. What _were you doing_ (you / do)?

B: I was here, but I _____ (play) with my son in the garden so I _____ (not hear) the doorbell.

Conversation 2

A: I heard you broke your leg. How _____ (it / happen)?

B: It happened when I _____ (climb) a mountain two weeks ago. I fell and I _____ (land) badly.

Conversation 3

A: Wendy told me you _____ (see) Jim last week.

B: Yes. I _____ (study) in the library, and he _____ (say) 'Hello'.

Conversation 4

A: I hear you crashed the car again. _____ (you / drive) too fast?

B: No! It wasn't my fault! I _____ (go) at thirty miles an hour when this other car suddenly _____ (come) out of a side street.

Conversation 5

A: I. _____ (see) you on your bicycle yesterday. Where _____ (you / go)?

B: I _____ (go) to the shops, but I _____ (dropped) my wallet on the way!

4A Look at the picture story. Match the verb phrases in the box with pictures 1–6.

> drop his ticket   try to sleep
> decide to use his mobile phone   go for a walk
> go through security   pay the taxi driver

B Complete the story with the past simple or the past continuous form of the verb phrases.

This is the story of Tim Bobo's first trip in an aeroplane. He was very excited, but as he was going out of the house he ¹ _dropped his ticket_ on the floor. He took a taxi to the airport, but while he ² _____, someone took his bag. Luckily there was nothing important in the bag. He checked in, but while he ³ _____, he found some keys in his pocket. Soon he was on the aeroplane. When it was taking off, he ⁴ _____ around the plane! The flight attendant told him to sit down immediately! Then soon after this he noticed that everyone seemed unhappy so he started singing. Unfortunately, the other passengers ⁵ _____ and they told him to be quiet. A few hours later, he made one more mistake: while the plane was landing, he ⁶ _____ his mobile phone!

5A ▶ 5.1 Listen and repeat the sentences you hear. Focus on the pronunciation of *was* and *were*.

B Read the audioscript on page 79. Listen and repeat the sentences again.

Read the audioscript on page 79.

LISTENING

6A ▶ 5.2 Listen to a story about a German tourist. Which map shows his journey, A or B?

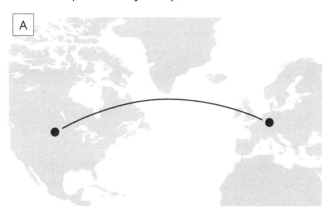

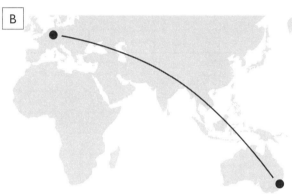

B Listen again. Are the statements true (T) or false (F)?

1 A German man wanted to visit his girlfriend in Sydney, Australia. ____
2 When he was booking his ticket, he made a mistake. ____
3 His flight took him to the wrong town in Australia. ____
4 He was wearing summer clothes because the weather in Montana was hot. ____
5 His parents and friends sent him warm clothes. ____
6 After a few days, he bought a ticket to Australia. ____

7A Read the sentences from the recording. Can you remember the rest of the next sentence?

1 A twenty-one-year-old German tourist called Tobi Gutt wanted to visit his girlfriend in Sydney, Australia. Unfortunately, _____.
2 When he looked at the plane to Sidney, he became confused. Strangely, _____.
3 A few friendly people helped him with food and drink until eventually, _____.

B ▶ 5.3 Listen to the sentences again. Write down the exact words that you hear.

VOCABULARY travel items

1A Use the clues to complete the crossword.

Across

3 You use this to take photos and put them on your computer. (two words)

7 You write names, addresses and ideas in this.

8 You put this on your head when the sun is very hot.

9 You pack your clothes in this. It is hard and sometimes has wheels.

Down

1 You wear these when it rains. (two words)

2 You wear these on your feet when you climb a mountain, or go for a long walk. (two words)

4 You buy these to remember the places you visited.

5 You use these to look at birds and animals that are far away.

6 You put important documents and money in this so they are safe. (two words)

B Use the words to complete the sentences.

1 I wrote her phone number in my _notebook_.

2 Before we leave for the airport, I'd like to buy some _____ for my friends.

3 It's very hot. You'll need to wear a _____.

4 These _____ _____ are new and my feet are really hurting.

5 It's raining. We'll have to wear some _____ _____.

6 Can you see that beautiful bird? Have a look through the _____.

7 My passport was in my _____ _____, but I took it off when I went swimming.

8 Thirty kilos. I'm afraid your _____ is too heavy. You'll need to pay extra.

9 I wanted to take some photos, but I left my _____ _____ at home.

GRAMMAR verb patterns

2 Underline the correct alternative.

1 I really enjoy *to read/reading* in bed before I go to sleep.

2 My brother wants *to see/seeing* you before he leaves.

3 We chose *to get/getting* married in Venice because that's where we first met.

4 My parents love *spend/spending* time with their grandchildren.

5 It always seems *to rain/raining* when I come to stay.

6 The company decided *to refund/refunding* the money we paid for the tickets.

7 We should avoid *to travel/travelling* when there is too much traffic.

8 The builders need *to finish/finishing* their work before we can paint the house.

9 We hope *to see/seeing* you again soon.

10 I must finish *to write/writing* this letter.

11 Just imagine *to live/living* in a place as beautiful as this!

12 I hate *to go/going* to the supermarket.

3 Make sentences with the prompts.

1 The children / love / play / on beach / in sun
The children love playing on the beach in the sun.

2 I / expect / hear from / travel agent / later today

3 we want / go / on holiday / but / we / too busy

4 we seem / go back / same place / every year

5 Alan chose / stay / in hotel

6 we enjoy / walk / and look at / the beautiful countryside

7 I decided / travel / on my own

8 we avoid / visit / tourist resorts / in summer

9 we need / book / our flights / before / prices / go up

READING

4A Read the article and match topics a)–e) with paragraphs 1–4.

a) making your own travel guides _____

b) reading about what happened to people on their holiday _____

c) holidays where you can work or volunteer _____

d) information about the weather in different countries _____

e) how to check the cost of your holiday _____

Top websites for travel tips

More and more people are booking their holidays on the internet, so we've looked at some useful websites to help you.

1 If you can't decide where to go on holiday, look at www.worldreviewer.com for some ideas. First, you can look at the interactive weather map, which tells you when different parts of the world are hot and sunny. Then, there is lots of information about different places to visit with photos and travellers' reviews. Here you can read about what other travellers *really* think about the place you are going to.

2 You can find great advice on which hotel to choose on www.tripadvisor.com. It has reviews and information on over 400,000 locations. You can also compare prices of different holidays to make sure you don't pay too much. And finally, there are photos of places to visit and fun travel stories, too.

3 If you want more than just a holiday, try www.thepodsite.co.uk. Here you can find out about holidays where you can work or volunteer, spend some time learning new skills and meeting new people. You can travel anywhere in the world to do all kinds of different jobs, from building in Tanzania to looking after elephants in Thailand. Just think what you could do.

4 Have you ever wanted to edit your own travel guide? Go to www.ivebeenthere.co.uk and you will be able to do just that. Using this site, you can create your own guides, choosing from the hundreds of different tips. Then just print it out and take it with you when you go. Make a guide for hostels in Southeast Asia, cafés in Italy, or family fun in New York. When you find another interesting tip, just add it to the list. Happy travelling.

B Find words or phrases in the article to match definitions 1–6.

1 something that involves communication with a computer, television, etc. (introduction): *internet*

2 someone's opinion in writing (paragraph 1): a _____

3 places (paragraph 2): _____

4 abilities/things you can do (paragraph 3): _____

5 make changes to improve a piece of writing (paragraph 4): _____

6 places where you can eat and sleep cheaply for a short time (paragraph 4): _____

C Which websites do you think these people should look at? Write 1, 2, 3 or 4.

1 Tom and Amanda want to travel around the world but they would like to do something useful. They both love working with animals. _____

2 Michail doesn't buy travel guides because they contain information which he doesn't need or which is out-of-date. _____

3 Felipe wants to hear about places from people who have actually been there. _____

4 Kamil doesn't mind where he goes to but he doesn't want to go anywhere which is too hot. _____

5 Eva wants to hear stories about what has happened to other travellers. _____

WRITING using sequencers

5A Look at the pictures of two stories. Put sentences a)–i) in the correct order to tell the stories.

a) ~~We had a great night out.~~

b) First, we met in a bar in town.

c) Finally, when we arrived, the hotel didn't have our reservation.

d) After that, we went dancing.

e) Then, our taxi broke down on the way to the hotel.

f) First, the flight was cancelled.

g) The holiday was a disaster.

h) Then, we went out for a pizza.

i) We waited, and after a while we had to fly to a different airport.

Story 1

a ____ , ____ , ____ , ____ , ____

FLIGHT CANCELLED

Story 2

____ , ____ , ____ , ____ , ____

B Write about a time when you went on holiday or had a good night out (50–100 words). Use the sequencers.

First Then After that/After a while Finally

VOCABULARY tourism

1 Match sentence beginnings 1–7 with endings a)–g).

1 There were a lot of __g__
2 I always wanted to be a tour ____
3 We went on a guided tour around the ____
4 They saw a lot of tourist attractions, including ____
5 I really enjoyed the boat trip ____
6 The best thing about Corsica is the scenery, which ____
7 Our boat took us under a ____

a) the History Museum and the National Art Gallery.
b) guide because I love showing people my city.
c) churches of Rome.
d) includes mountains, beaches and forests.
e) waterfall, which was probably fifty metres high.
f) down the River Nile.
g) tourists in our hotel.

FUNCTION directions

2 Underline the correct alternative. Where no word is necessary, choose (–).

1 For the Red Duck bar, go straight *in/over/on* and you can't miss it.
2 Go *(–)/for/along* the main road until you see the sports field.
3 To reach the train station, you need to go *up/through/in* the centre of town.
4 Keep going *(–)/on/by* until you reach the corner of King's Road.
5 You'll find the police station *up/at/of* the corner.
6 Walk for two minutes and you'll see the school in front *of/by/to* you.
7 Take *to/(–)/on* the second left after the library and you'll see my house.
8 For the post office, go *past/through/on* the turning for the station.

3A ▶ 5.4 Look at the map and listen to the directions. Where is the man trying to go?

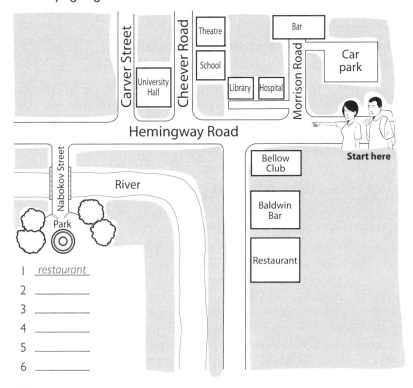

1 _restaurant_
2 ____
3 ____
4 ____
5 ____
6 ____

B Read the audioscript on page 79 and check your answers.

LEARN TO show/check understanding

4A Put the words in the correct order to complete the conversations.

Conversation 1

A: Excuse me. _____? (help / you / me / can) I'm looking for the Science Museum.
B: Go straight on. _____. (can't / you / it / miss)
A: OK, so it's easy! _____? (map / you / the / me / on / can / show)
B: Yes, of course.

Conversation 2

A: Excuse me. I'm trying to find the internet café. _____? (the / this / way / right / is)
B: Yes. Keep going. _____. (it / see / of / front / in / you / you'll)
A: _____? (walk / I / can)
B: Yes, you can. _____. (about / minutes / it / ten / takes)

Conversation 3

A: _____ to the tube? (far / it / is)
B: No. It's about two minutes' walk.
A: OK. _____? (to / need / left / so / the / go / at / I / cinema)
B: That's right. It's easy!

B ▶ 5.5 Listen and check.

VOCABULARY health

1 Complete the texts with the words in the box.

> walking   junk   fizzy   working   stressed   life   miss
> exercise   caffeine   fresh   frozen

I try to eat healthily. I buy lots of ¹_____ fruit and vegetables and use these to cook with. I don't like to eat ²_____ food, like hamburgers or packets of crisps. I ³_____ every day by ⁴_____ the dog.

I'm not as healthy as I would like to be. It's difficult when you live a city ⁵_____.
I'm always too busy. I spend most of my time ⁶_____ with computers, and dealing with people's problems. So, I'm quite ⁷_____, and I don't eat very well. I don't have time. I buy ⁸_____ food and put it in the microwave.

Food isn't very important to me really. Sometimes I don't eat all day. I usually ⁹_____ breakfast, because I get up too late. And during the day I don't really think about eating. I'm addicted to ¹⁰_____ though! I drink about ten cups of coffee a day and have lots of ¹¹_____ drinks, too.

GRAMMAR present perfect + *for/since*

2 Complete the conversations with the present perfect form of the verb in brackets.

1 A: How long __has__ Carlos __worked__ here? (work)
   B: About four years. He _____ here for four years. (be)

2 A: Did you see that comedy film last night?
   B: Yes, it was the funniest film I _____ ever _____! (watch)

3 A: Do you know where Morris _____ _____? (go)
   B: No. I _____ _____ him all day. (not / see)

4 A: _____ you _____ your homework? (finish)
   B: No. I _____ _____ it yet. (not / start)

5 A: Do you know if my parcel _____ _____? (arrive)
   B: Just a minute. I'll have a look for you.

6 A: _____ you _____ your watch? (find)
   B: Yes, it was under the sofa.

7 A: How long _____ you _____ Marissa? (know)
   B: Not very long. We _____ _____ friends for long at all. (not / be)

8 A: _____ you _____ my news? (hear)
   B: No. _____ you _____ to leave your job? (decide)

3 Make sentences with the prompts using the present perfect with *for/since*.

1 I / know / Imelda / ages
   *I've known Imelda for ages.*_____

2 he / work / for that company / six months
   _____

3 we / live / Turkey / 2006
   _____

4 I / not be / to the cinema / a long time
   _____

5 they / be here / two months now
   _____

6 I / not clean / the house / last Monday
   _____

7 she / not listen to / that music / she was a teenager
   _____

8 we / not hear / from him / he left
   _____

9 Bob / be a builder / more than forty years
   _____

10 the phone / not ring / 10 o'clock
    _____

11 I / want / to climb a mountain / I was a child
    _____

4 Underline the correct alternative.

Interviewer: So, Joy, you *have started*/*started* the Laugh to Live organisation in 2003.

Joy: That's right.

Interviewer: Why [1]*did you start*/*have you started* it? What [2]*did you want*/*have you wanted* to do?

Joy: I [3]*started*/*have started* Laugh to Live because I [4]*felt*/*have felt* I had something I wanted to share with people. In my life I [5]*have lived*/*lived* and worked in four different countries, in four different continents, so [6]*I've had*/*I had* a lot of experience and [7]*I've worked*/*I worked* with people from all over the world.

Interviewer: And what have you learnt from these experiences?

Joy: I think I've learnt something very important in life. Most people just want to live a simple, happy life. But they don't know where to look for happiness. Years ago, when I [8]*travelled*/*have travelled* to Africa, I [9]*met*/*have met* poor children in the jungle who had nothing. But they had the biggest smiles [10]*I have ever seen*/*I saw*. This taught me that happiness and laughter are inside us all. I have a few techniques which I [11]*have used*/*used* to help people learn to laugh more often, especially when things are difficult in their lives. And because they now laugh more, they [12]*have become*/*became* happier people.

Interviewer: Thank you, Joy. And good luck with your work.

5A ▶ 6.1 **Listen and tick the sentence you hear.**

1 a) I've known her for ages.
   b) She's known it for ages.
2 a) They travelled a lot.
   b) They've travelled a lot.
3 a) He's never seen it before.
   b) He's never been here before.
4 a) Nothing has changed.
   b) Nothing changed.
5 a) I've worked in other countries.
   b) I worked in other countries.

B **Listen again. Practise saying the sentences.**

6A ▶ 6.2 **Listen to the first part of a news report and choose the correct option to complete the sentences, a), b) or c).**

1 The reporter went to a table tennis centre for people aged _____.
   a) under fifteen   b) under fifty   c) over fifty
2 People should eat _____ portions of fruit and vegetables a day.
   a) five   b) one   c) eight
3 Living a healthy life can add _____ years to your life.
   a) four   b) fourteen   c) forty

B ▶ 6.3 **Listen to the whole report. Are the statements true (T) or false (F)?**

1 The woman plays table tennis four times a week. _____
2 She says it gives her a great feeling. _____
3 Scientists studied 20,000 people for fifteen years. _____
4 They found that people who don't smoke, exercise regularly and eat lots of fruit and vegetables every day live longer. _____
5 Doctors say if you want to see changes to your health, you need to make big changes to your lifestyle. _____
6 The second woman says she always eats five portions of fruit and vegetables a day. _____

C **Match the words/phrases in bold in 1–5 with definitions a)–e).**

1 I feel **fabulous**.
2 Scientists have now **worked out** that you can live longer if you have a healthy lifestyle.
3 ... who do **regular** exercise, and those who eat lots of fruit and vegetables a day ...
4 It's **never too late to start**.
5 It's **part of the fun**.

a) once a week/once a month, etc.
b) you can still do it now
c) very good/wonderful
d) one of the things you enjoy
e) calculated

VOCABULARY food

1 Find seven types of fruit using these letters. You can use the letters more than once.

2 Complete the words in the menu and the recipe.

The Terrace Bistro Menu

Chef's choice

Tender baby ¹ch_ck_n grilled in a light herb sauce with strips of ²b_c_n. Served with rice and ³br_cc_l_.

Meat-eater's delight

⁴B___fst___k marinaded in a cream and ⁵sp_n_ch sauce. Served with ⁶p_t_t_es.

King's feast

Roasted ⁷l_g _f l_mb with rice, ⁸c_bb_ge and freshly diced ⁹c___rg_tt_s.

Pasta Atlantica

Fry 50 g of ¹⁰shr_mps in a pan with a little butter.

~

Add ¹¹_n___ns and ¹²g_rl_c to the pan.

~

Boil 50 g of ¹³m_ss_ls.

~

Cook the pasta.

~

Mix the pasta and seafood and put in a tray.

~

Add a layer of ¹⁴ch___s_ on top and cook in the oven for twenty minutes until brown.

GRAMMAR *may, might, will*

3 Circle the best option to complete the conversations, a), b) or c).

1 A: What are you doing this weekend?
   B: I'm not sure. We _____ go to the seafood restaurant.
   a) may   b) will   c) won't

2 A: Will that café on Wardour Street be open tomorrow?
   B: I don't know. It _____ be.
   a) will   b) won't   c) might

3 A: I've cooked little Johnny some vegetables for tonight's dinner.
   B: Thanks, but he _____ eat them.
   a) might   b) will   c) won't

4 A: Can I try your food?
   B: Be careful. It _____ be too hot for you.
   a) may   b) won't   c) may not

5 A: Do we need to buy any ingredients for this recipe?
   B: Maybe. We _____ have enough garlic. Can you check?
   a) won't   b) might not   c) will

6 A: You know Melissa's a vegetarian, don't you?
   B: OK, I _____ cook meat.
   a) won't   b) will   c) may

7 A: Are you going to that new bar before you leave town?
   B: I don't know. I hope so, but we _____ have time.
   a) won't   b) will   c) may not

8 A: What are your predictions for food in the future?
   B: The good news is I think it _____ be more healthy.
   a) might not   b) will   c) won't

4 Put the words in the correct order to make six predictions about food.

1 more / eat / know / people / what / about / will / they
   People will know more about what they eat.

2 future / we / animals / the / eat / won't / in
   _____

3 eat / food / we / more / organic / may
   _____

4 might / illegal / junk / become / food
   _____

5 fatter / people / West / will / the / get / in
   _____

6 the / left / may / there / sea / not / be / in / fish / any
   _____

READING

5A Read the text and match pictures A–D with paragraphs 1–4.

HOW TO EAT LESS

Brian Wansink of Cornell University did some **experiments** to show why we eat too much. Here are four of the results:

1 __ Wansink invited a group of people to lunch. He told half of them they were eating something expensive and delicious, 'Royal Italian Bolognese with haricots verts'. He told the other half they were eating cheap food from a can. In fact, both groups ate the same food. He secretly watched them. The ones who thought they were eating expensive food ate much more than the others.

CONCLUSION: if people think the food sounds good and it is expensive, they think it tastes better.

2 __ Wansink did an experiment at a cinema in Chicago. He gave everyone a free bag of popcorn, but the popcorn was old and tasted bad. Most people noticed this, but they still ate almost all of it.

CONCLUSION: how much we eat depends on: where we are (in the cinema); what we are doing (**concentrating** on a film, not on food); what other people are doing (eating popcorn). These things may be more important than the taste of the food.

3 __ Wansink went to a sports bar and gave the customers free chicken. The waiters cleaned half the tables every few minutes and took away the chicken bones. No one cleaned the other tables. The people with clean tables ate seven pieces of chicken, **on average**. The others ate five.

CONCLUSION: when we see how much we're eating, we eat less. When we can't see how much we're eating, we eat more.

4 __ Wansink invited people to watch a video. He gave them each a bag of sweets to eat during the film. Half the bags had sweets with seven different colours; the other bags had sweets with ten different colours. The people whose sweets had more colours ate forty-three more sweets than the others.

CONCLUSION: when there is a big **variety**, people want to try everything. So they eat more.

B Circle the best option to answer the questions, a) or b).

1 Why did Wansink do the experiments?
   a) to improve the food we eat
   b) to discover why people eat more than they need

2 How did Wansink do his experiments?
   a) he asked questions about what people ate
   b) he gave free food to people and then watched them

3 Who ate more?
   a) the people who thought their food was expensive
   b) the people who thought their food was cheap

4 What was interesting about Wansink's popcorn?
   a) it didn't taste good   b) it had different colours

5 Who ate more chicken?
   a) the people with messy tables
   b) the people with clean tables

6 Who ate more sweets?
   a) the people whose sweets had seven colours
   b) the people whose sweets had ten colours

C Find words in bold in the text to match definitions 1–4.

1 giving your attention to something _____
2 many different types of things _____
3 scientific tests to find information _____
4 based on a calculation of 'what most people do'
   _____

WRITING sentence structure

6A Connect the two sentences. Use *and*, *but* or *when*. Use each word twice.

1 I have always liked cooking. I cook every day.
   _____

2 I was very young. I cooked my first meal.
   _____

3 I don't eat much meat. I eat a lot of fish.
   _____

4 I was working as a chef in a horrible hotel. I decided to open my own restaurant.
   _____

5 I don't drink alcohol. I use a little wine in some of the dishes I prepare.
   _____

6 I like meeting customers at my restaurant. I ask them about the food.
   _____

B Write the words *and* and *also* in the correct places.

1 My favourite types of food are pasta fresh fish. I like fruit.

2 Every morning I buy vegetables herbs from the market. I buy meat there.

3 I find that the food in the market is fresher better quality. It's cheaper.

VOCABULARY illness

1 Use the clues to complete the crossword.

Across

5 It's very painful. I'm taking _____.

7 She fell down the stairs and she's _____ her leg.

9 The doctor's given me some _____ to stop the infection.

10 I had to go to the hospital for an _____.

Down

1 We've got some _____ for your cough.

2 I don't feel well. I think I've caught a _____.

3 I'm tired. I need to get some _____.

4 He feels hot. I think he's got a _____.

6 My head hurts. I've got a _____.

8 I can't speak. I've got a _____ throat.

Crossword grid with 1 Down spelling M E D I C I N E

FUNCTION seeing the doctor

2 Match sentence beginnings 1–11 with endings a)–k).

Doctor

1 What's the
2 How long have you
3 Where does it
4 Can I have a
5 It's nothing to
6 I'll give you some

a) hurt?
b) pills/antibiotics/medicine.
c) had this problem?
d) worry about.
e) matter?
f) look?

Patient

7 I feel
8 It
9 It's
10 I'm worried
11 I can't

g) about my leg.
h) very painful.
i) sleep.
j) hurts when I walk.
k) sick/terrible.

3A Some of the lines in the conversations have words missing. Write the missing word or put a tick if the sentence is correct.

Conversation 1

Doctor: Good morning. How can I help? ✓

Woman: I'm worried / my leg. *about*

Doctor: Your leg? What's matter with it?

Woman: Well, very painful. It hurts when I walk.

Doctor: I see. How long have you the problem?

Woman: Since yesterday.

Doctor: Can I a look?

Woman: Yes, of course.

Conversation 2

Doctor: Hello. What's matter, Mr Smith?

Man: I feel terrible.

Doctor: All right. Where does hurt?

Man: Everywhere. And can't sleep.

Doctor: Ah. Have you got temperature?

Man: I don't know.

Doctor: OK. Can I have look?

Man: Yes, of course.

Doctor: That's fine. It's nothing worry about.

Man: But I feel terrible!

B ▶ 6.4 Listen to the conversations and check your answers.

LEARN TO predict information

4A Predict what the doctor says using the prompts.

Conversation 1

Doctor: Good afternoon. ¹_____? (matter)

Patient: I've got a sore throat and a headache.

Doctor: I see. ²_____? (long)

Patient: About two weeks.

Doctor: ³_____? (temperature)

Patient: Yes. It's 38.5, so I've taken some aspirin.

Doctor: I see. I think ⁴_____. (cold) You need ⁵_____ (rest) and ⁶_____. (drinks)

Conversation 2

Patient: I think I've broken my arm.

Doctor: Oh dear. ¹_____? (look)

Patient: Yes. Here you are.

Doctor: So, ²_____? (where / hurt)

Patient: Here, and here.

Doctor: ³_____? (how / do)

Patient: I fell over.

Doctor: I think you should ⁴_____. (go / hospital / X-ray)

B ▶ 6.5 Listen to the conversations and check your answers.

GRAMMAR present perfect + *ever/never* or past simple

1 **Put the verb in brackets into the correct form of the present perfect or the past simple.**

1 He has *never travelled* (never / travel) abroad.
2 I _____ (never / visit) Amsterdam, but I'd like to go in the future.
3 My grandparents _____ (come) to this country in 1956.
4 _____ you ever _____ (see) a ghost?
5 So far on this trip, we _____ (be) to ten countries.
6 Jane _____ (get) her exam results yesterday.
7 When you lived in Germany, _____ you _____ (go) to Frankfurt?
8 I hear Lindsay's girlfriend is very nice, but I _____ (not / meet) her yet.
9 I _____ (not / hear) you come in last night.
10 That girl started playing tennis three years ago, but she _____ (never / win) a match!
11 I know your mother likes foreign food, but _____ she _____ (ever / eat) snails?

GRAMMAR *can*, *have to*, *must*

2 **Circle the correct option to complete the text.**

To enter the university library, everyone ¹___ show a current student or staff ID. No exceptions. To borrow books, you ²___ take the books to the front desk and show your ID. You ³___ take out a maximum of eight books. There are some books that you ⁴___ take out. These are marked Reference Only. There is a late fee of 20p per day, but you ⁵___ renew the books online for an extra week. If you have renewed the books before the due date, you ⁶___ pay the fee. To order books that are not in the library, you ⁷___ fill in the form at the front desk marked Special Orders. You ⁸___ write the full name of the book, the author and the ISBN. We ⁹___ guarantee a date for the arrival of these books. You ¹⁰___ write in the books; anyone who is caught doing this will pay a fine.

1 a) must   b) have to   c) can
2 a) doesn't have to b) has to   c) have to
3 a) can't   b) mustn't   c) can
4 a) don't have to   b) can't   c) have to
5 a) can   b) has to   c) don't have to
6 a) don't have to   b) must   c) can't
7 a) has to   b) don't have to   c) have to
8 a) can't   b) must   c) don't have to
9 a) doesn't have to b) can't   c) has to
10 a) don't have to   b) has to   c) mustn't

FUNCTION giving advice

3 **Complete the conversation with words in the box.**

should think why idea suppose shouldn't sure should

Ella: What do you think I ¹ *should* wear to the interview? ² _____ I wear jeans?
Beth: No, you ³ _____! You have to try and look smart.
Ella: I ⁴ _____ so. What about this? This dress will be OK, won't it?
Beth: I'm not ⁵ _____ about that. It's a bit short.
Ella: Oh yes, maybe you're right.
Beth: I ⁶ _____ you should wear trousers and a jacket.
Ella: A jacket? I don't think that's a good ⁷ _____. I haven't worn a jacket since I was at school!
Beth: I've got a nice jacket. Here. ⁸ _____ don't you try this on?

GRAMMAR past simple and past continuous

4 **Underline the correct alternative.**

This story ¹*happened/was happening* while Guillermo Diaz ²*studied/was studying* English at a community college in the USA. Diaz was a very bad student who never attended classes. One evening when he ³*sat/was sitting* in a bar, he ⁴*saw/was seeing* another student, Arturo, who told him about an exam the next day. Arturo said the exam was in Room 52, but Diaz thought he said Room 62. The next day, when Diaz was doing the exam, he ⁵*realised/was realising* that he didn't know any of the answers. He tried to ask another student for the answers while the professor ⁶*didn't look/wasn't looking*, but the other student ⁷*didn't help/wasn't helping* him. The exam ⁸*had/was having* multiple-choice questions so Diaz guessed all of the answers. A week later, while Diaz ⁹*watched/was watching* TV at home, he ¹⁰*received/was receiving* his results by post. He scored 100 percent in the exam ... on American history!

GRAMMAR verb patterns

5 **Each sentence has a verb missing. Complete the sentences with verbs in the box in the infinitive or the *-ing* form.**

be drive cook lose get up clean write shop

        to be
1 We expect╱home by 2.30.
2 I want a great book so I can become famous!
3 I need early tomorrow so I'm going to bed now.
4 We usually avoid at this time because of all the traffic.
5 Do you enjoy meals for large groups of people?
6 They decided the whole house after the party.
7 She loves for clothes.
8 I always seem something when I travel – usually my plane ticket.

FUNCTION asking for and giving directions

6 Match sentence beginnings 1–8 with endings a)–h).

1 The restaurant is in	a) bridge.
2 Go along	b) through the centre of town.
3 Take the	c) second right.
4 Keep going until	d) the main road.
5 You'll see the bar	e) you reach the cinema.
6 Go	f) at the corner.
7 Cross the	g) front of you.
8 Go straight	h) on.

GRAMMAR present perfect + for/since

7 Cross out the alternative which is not possible in each sentence.

1 They have been waiting here *since the office opened/for hours/since ten minutes.*

2 I've played the guitar *since 2007/for six years/since months.*

3 They haven't visited us *since last Christmas/for January/for several weeks.*

4 Have you known Sourav *since you were at school/for a long time/since years?*

5 I haven't eaten *for the last meal/for hours/since last night.*

6 We've lived in the USA *for a very long time/since the government changed/for now.*

7 My team hasn't won a game *for three years/since months/since they won the cup last year.*

8 Kim has been a nurse *since last year/for December/since she left university.*

9 Svetlana hasn't spoken to me *since two years/for three weeks/since we broke up.*

GRAMMAR may, might, will

8 Find and correct the mistakes. There is a mistake in each sentence.

1 I don't will go to the cinema tonight because I'm busy.

2 I may to send her an email.

3 We not might have time to go to the museum.

4 The weather report on TV said there might to be storms.

5 Joshua may not be go to the game.

6 I'm might be late to class tonight.

FUNCTION seeing the doctor

9A Who says the phrases a)–f)? The doctor (D) or the patient (P)?

a) How long have you had this problem? _____

b) It's very painful. _____

c) What's the problem? _____

d) But I'm worried about missing work. _____

e) Doctor, I feel terrible. _____

f) Where does it hurt? _____

B Complete the conversation with phrases a)–f).

Doctor: Good morning. [1]_____

Patient: [2]_____ I have a backache all the time, and it hurts when I walk.

Doctor: I see. [3]_____

Patient: About two weeks.

Doctor: Can I have a look? [4]_____

Patient: Here. [5]_____ Sometimes I can't sleep because of the pain.

Doctor: OK, I'll give you some medicine for it. And you shouldn't do any heavy work for a few weeks.

Patient: [6]_____ I'm a builder.

Doctor: You need to rest for at least two weeks. I'll write a note. OK?

Patient: OK. Thanks, doctor.

C ▶ RC2.1 Listen and check.

VOCABULARY revision

10 Write a word from units 4–6 to match the definitions. The first letter of each word is given.

1 a_____: you make this when you agree a time to visit the doctor or dentist

2 b_____: look through these to see things far away

3 c_____: it's in coffee and tea and it makes you feel active

4 d_____: you make this when you decide to do something

5 e_____: a formal test

6 f_____: describes drinks with gas

7 g_____: we play these (e.g. football, tennis)

8 h_____: students do this after school for their teacher

9 i_____ _____: the subject of computers, called 'IT'

10 j_____ _____: food that isn't healthy because it has lots of fat or sugar

11 k_____: a bag of medicines, bandages, etc., to treat ill/injured people (a first aid _____)

12 l_____: books, poems, plays

13 m_____: a fast form of transport with two wheels

14 n_____ _____: a person who learnt a language as their first language when they were a baby

15 o_____: connected to the internet

16 p_____: a small round thing, medicine that you put in your mouth and swallow

17 r_____: a bag you carry on your back

18 s_____: an object that you keep to remember a place you visited

19 t_____: a type of transport; an electric street train

20 u_____: a type of clothes worn by some professions (e.g. nurses) or schoolchildren

21 v_____: a type of food (e.g. potato, carrot, onion)

22 w_____: a type of clothes that don't allow water to enter

23 y_____: an activity that helps relax the body and mind

TEST

Circle the correct option to complete the sentences.

1 Everyone likes that film, but I _____ it.

a) saw   b) don't see   c) haven't seen

2 I started writing ten years ago, but I _____ anything.

a) have never published   b) don't publish
c) didn't publish

3 He _____ his girlfriend in 1998.

a) did meet   b) met   c) has met

4 You _____ have a passport to get into the country.

a) has to   b) have to   c) can

5 She _____ do any homework tonight so she can come with us.

a) doesn't have to   b) can   c) has to

6 You _____ see the dentist about that tooth.

a) should   b) try   c) don't

7 _____ don't we go to that new restaurant tonight?

a) How   b) Should   c) Why

8 She has to _____ an appointment with a dentist.

a) start   b) do   c) make

9 The exam was difficult, but I _____ my best.

a) did   b) made   c) worked

10 I usually _____ new words in a dictionary.

a) study up   b) look up   c) take up

11 I _____ along the street when I met Dave.

a) walked   b) am walking   c) was walking

12 The radio was on, but nobody _____.

a) wasn't listening   b) was listening c) listened

13 She _____ her arm while she was skiing.

a) did break   b) broke   c) was breaking

14 They expect _____ this game easily.

a) win   b) winning   c) to win

15 Try to avoid _____ a lot of noise because your brother is sleeping.

a) making   b) to make   c) make

16 I've decided _____ law.

a) studying   b) study   c) to study

17 Keep walking until you _____ the river.

a) at   b) reach   c) get

18 The bar is in front _____ you.

a) to   b) by   c) of

19 Did you travel _____ train?

a) on   b) by   c) the

20 We should take _____ clothes because it's going to rain.

a) watertight   b) watery   c) waterproof

21 I've known Rami _____ my first year at college.

a) since   b) for   c) because

22 She has worked with us _____ three years.

a) since   b) by   c) for

23 They haven't been here _____ 1987.

a) for   b) since   c) until

24 You _____ need a special visa, but I'm not certain.

a) will   b) have   c) might

25 In the future, cars _____ use oil because it will be too expensive.

a) will   b) can't   c) won't

26 I _____ come to the lesson because I have to work late.

a) may not   b) am not   c) will

27 I _____ a headache.

a) am   b) have   c) make

28 Where does it _____?

a) hurts   b) hurt   c) pain

29 I _____ yoga twice a week.

a) do   b) play   c) exercise

30 We try to _____ some exercise every day.

a) make   b) play   c) do

TEST RESULT /30

40

VOCABULARY verbs + prepositions

1 Underline the correct alternative.

1 James didn't like working in an office, so he gave *on/up/with* his job and decided to travel *for/to/around* the world.

2 I'm moving *to/on/in* the USA in August. At the moment I'm waiting *of/about/for* my visa.

3 I was born in Pakistan in a village with no school. I've always dreamed *in/about/for* going *to/back/from* there to open a school for the children.

4 Sal's thinking *in/to/about* doing an art course. She's looking *about/in/for* someone who can teach her how to paint.

2 Match the sentence beginnings 1–7 with endings a)–g).

1 When are you going	a) to Berlin because they want to be near his family.
2 I'm looking	b) up trying to contact him.
3 She's travelling	c) back home? Have you booked your ticket yet?
4 He's OK. He's waiting	d) about it for a while and tell me later?
5 They moved	e) for my bag. Have you seen it anywhere?
6 He never answers my calls, so I've given	f) around America at the moment on a bus.
7 Do you want to think	g) for a friend.

GRAMMAR used to

3 Complete the sentences with the correct form of *used to* and a verb from the box.

~~visit~~	like	spend	come	stay	run	study
read	be					

1 We *didn't use to visit* our cousins very often when we were young.

2 I _____ a lot of books as a child, but now I only read the newspapers.

3 _____ you _____ French at school?

4 There _____ a cinema in the town centre, but it's closed now.

5 _____ you _____ a lot of time with your grandparents?

6 We _____ in a small hotel by the sea every summer.

7 My father was always very fit. He _____ eight kilometres every morning.

8 He _____ her because he thought she was rude. Now he's fallen madly in love!

9 Tourists _____ here very often, but now it's very popular.

4 Read the text and look at the pictures. Use the prompts to write sentences with *used to/didn't use to*.

Ten years ago

James Turnbull and Harry Potts left their office jobs in London to move to Tobago and open a bar on the beach. Now, ten years later, they own two hotels, a restaurant and a nightclub. When James told his colleagues at work about his plans, they thought he was crazy. So, when the pair opened their first bar, they called it The Crazy Bar. It's been a great success.

Now

1 James and Harry / work / London.
   James and Harry used to work in London.

2 they / dream / about a life on the beach
   _____

3 they / sit in traffic / on the way to the office
   _____

4 Harry / wear a suit / to go to work
   _____

5 James / not spend his time / sitting on the beach
   _____

6 they / not eat / tropical fruit for breakfast
   _____

7 they / not wear / shorts and a T-shirt to work
   _____

8 they / not go / surfing at the end of the day
   _____

9 James's colleagues / think / he was crazy
   _____

5A ▶ 7.1 Listen and complete the sentences.

1 She _____ very shy.

2 I _____ a car.

3 My granddad _____ me sweets.

4 I never _____ at school.

5 They _____ in America.

6 Did you _____ to the cinema?

B ▶ 7.2 Listen and repeat the sentences. Focus on the pronunciation of *used to* and *didn't use to*.

READING

6 Read the article and match pictures A–F with paragraphs 1–6.

A

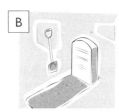
B

C
LIVE AID ▶

D

E
SALE

F

BEFORE THEY WERE FAMOUS ...

1 ___ Did you know that Rod Stewart worked as a grave digger or that Mick Jagger was once a porter in a mental hospital? If you find you are stuck in a rut and dream about being famous, don't give up. Some of the most famous celebrities started their working lives in some very simple jobs.

2 ___ When Madonna first arrived in New York looking for fame and fortune, she only had $35 in her pocket. She took a job working at Dinky Donuts in Times Square, but later lost her job for squirting jam at one of the customers.

3 ___ Bob Geldof had many different jobs before he started working as a music journalist. While working in London, one of his jobs was as a hot dog salesman in Soho. In 1975, he found fame as the lead singer of the Irish band, The Boomtown Rats. He has strong political ideas too, and he organises concerts like Live Aid to try and change the situation in Africa.

4 ___ Before being an actor, Johnny Depp used to sell pens. He used to telephone people to sell them pens with their names printed on them. But he didn't enjoy the job, so sometimes he tried using different voices on the telephone to make the job more interesting.

5 ___ When Texas released their first single, Sharleen Spiteri was working as a hairdresser in Glasgow. She says she loved the job because her clients told her such shocking gossip. 'I was a great hairdresser,' she says. 'People told me everything!'

6 ___ Before Annie Lennox became famous, she worked in a bookshop. She then spent time singing in pubs and clubs and worked as a waitress in Hampstead, London, where she met Dave Stewart. They eventually formed The Eurythmics and went on to have many chart successes.

7 Read the article again. Are the sentences true (T) or false (F)?

1 When Madonna first arrived in New York, she was a famous dancer. ____

2 Bob Geldof became famous for starting a successful hot dog business in London. ____

3 Johnny Depp worked in sales. ____

4 He thought the job was boring. ____

5 Sharleen Spiteri didn't enjoy working as a hairdresser because she had to deal with customers' problems. ____

6 Annie Lennox met her partner Dave Stewart in a bookshop. ____

WRITING paragraphs

8 Read the article and number the sentences in each paragraph in the correct order, 1–3.

1 introduces the main idea

2 supports the idea

3 finishes or concludes the paragraph

STUCK IN A RUT?

2 If you're doing the same thing every day, maybe you're stuck in a rut, and you need to do something about it.

3 Here are some tips.

1 How often do you wake up in the morning excited about what the day will bring?

Set new goals

___ What exactly do you want to change in your life?

___ Writing down your goals is the first step towards achieving them.

___ Decide on some new goals to help you achieve this change and write them down.

Do something different

___ Try not doing something for a while (like not watching television for one week).

___ This will give you time to try doing something different.

___ Do you spend a lot of your time doing the same things every day?

Think about now

___ If you try to focus on the present, things will seem easier.

___ And don't worry about things which haven't happened yet.

___ Don't spend too much time thinking about the past and worrying about decisions you have already made.

Learn a new skill

___ Also the process of learning something new will make you feel better and more satisfied.

___ So, if you learn a new skill, you'll find you can quickly get out of a rut.

___ Learning a new skill might give you new opportunities in life.

VOCABULARY collocations

1 Complete the words in the news headlines.

1
> **KENYAN SCIENTIST FINDS A WAY TO C_u__r__e_ CANCER**

2
> **FILM DIRECTOR MAKES D_____Y ABOUT AMAZON TRIBES**

3
> **'HOUSE ON FIRE HERO' S_____ THREE LIVES**

4
> **EXCLUSIVE! FILM STAR TELLS ALL: 'HOW I B_____ FAMOUS IN HOLLYWOOD'**

5
> **SHOCK AS TOP LONDON LAWYER IS A_____D FOR MURDER**

6
> **PRINCE DECIDES TO S___D SIX MONTHS ABROAD**

7
> **A HUNDRED-YEAR-OLD ACTOR PLAYS HIS FINAL R___E IN FILM**

2 Cross out the alternative which is not possible in each sentence.

1 The doctor cured *the illness/medicine/Mrs Jones.*
2 This is one way to become *film/famous/successful.*
3 The killer spent *twenty years in prison/time abroad/many people.*
4 She plays *an important part in the film/a role/a theatre.*
5 In the book, Mr Travis saves *his son's life/some money/ a long way.*
6 I really wanted to make *a play/a film/a documentary.*
7 Miss Maxwell has been arrested for *murder/thief/ a crime.*

GRAMMAR purpose, cause and result

3 Find and correct the mistakes. There are mistakes in eight of the sentences.

1 I worked hard for to pass my exams.
2 She was angry because we didn't do our homework.
3 I play a lot of sport because want to stay fit.
4 He drove for six hours to meeting you.
5 The bus was late so that we walked.
6 I spent time abroad because of I like travelling.
7 I'm going to the restaurant for meet my friends.
8 He wanted to become a film star so he went to Hollywood.
9 I went to the shop for buying the book.
10 I live miles from my office but so I get a train to work.

4 Complete the texts with *to*, *so* or *because*.

1 John Klimt changed his name eight times _____ he wanted to have the names of his great-grandparents. He wanted to include the women too, _____ for a short time he was called Sara, Katrina, Jessica and Margit!

2 In 2005, a town called Clark, Texas, changed its name to Dish. Why? _____ in 2005, DISH TV network offered ten years of free satellite and digital TV to everyone if the town changed its name. _____ the town's residents agreed to do it!

3 In 2006, Australian singer Rebecca Swift changed her hair colour every day for 365 days. Why? _____ be different. She is a fan of Madonna, who changes her image all the time, _____ Rebecca copied her.

4 Epi Taione, a Tongan rugby player, changed his name to Paddy Power during the 2007 Rugby World Cup. Paddy Power is a company which gave money to the Tongan team, _____ Taione changed his name _____ say thank you!

LISTENING

5A ▶ **7.3 Listen to a radio programme and circle the correct option to complete the sentences.**

1 The programme is about people who change their _____.
   a) job   b) nationality   c) name

2 People have _____ for changing.
   a) many reasons   b) three reasons   c) one main reason

3 The programme explains that Muhammad Ali's _____.
   a) original name was Cassius Clay
   b) first religion was Christian   c) name is Arabic

4 The programme mentions several famous _____.
   a) sportspeople   b) writers   c) singers

5 Many people change their names when they move to a new country, especially in _____.
   a) Europe   b) the USA and the UK   c) films

6 The programme mentions Angelina Jolie's _____.
   a) childhood   b) father   c) children

Muhammad Ali

Angelina Jolie

George Michael

B Listen again and complete the notes.

When a woman gets ¹_____ she might want to go back to her original name.

Cassius Clay became Muhammad Ali because he changed his ²_____.

The name Freddie Mercury is probably easier to ³_____ than Farookh Balsara.

Another reason people want to change their name is to identify with a new ⁴_____.

Angelina Jolie's father is an ⁵_____. Oprah Winfrey is called Oprah because there was a ⁶_____ on her birth certificate.

C Read audio script 7.3 on page 80 and find words to match the definitions below.

1 when a husband and wife end their marriage _____

2 the person who sings the most in a band _____

3 to feel that you understand or have a connection with someone or something _____

4 a document that shows when and where you were born _____

5 a person who goes to live in a different country _____

6 a sportsperson who fights in matches _____

7 to keep a distance between two things _____

D Complete the sentences with the words in the box.

got divorced   give (an) example
real name   lead singer   identify with
birth certificate

1 To get a passport, you need to show your _____ _____.

2 I've lived in ten countries, but I don't really _____ _____ any of them.

3 That's a good point. Can you _____ an _____?

4 The actor Michael Caine's _____ _____ is Maurice Micklewhite.

5 They got married, but four years later they _____ _____.

6 Bono is the _____ _____ of the band U2.

VOCABULARY facilities

1 Use the clues to complete the crossword.

Across

6 Let's meet for a coffee in the _____.

8 Professor Morris is giving a presentation in the _____ theatre at 2p.m.

9 I'm going to the _____ to borrow a book.

10 I want to buy a dictionary. I think there's a _____ _____ over there. (2 words)

Down

1 Do you know where the _____ _____ is? I need to make a photocopy of this form. (2 words)

2 I need to register for my course. Is this the _____ _____? (2 words)

3 I'll take you to the _____ _____. They can tell you about your accommodation. (2 words)

4 When you go in to the building, ask for Mr Kubovsky at the _____ _____. (2 words)

5 Is there a _____ _____ near here? I need to buy a notebook. (2 words)

7 Our lesson is in a different _____ today.

FUNCTION finding out information

2 Read the conversations. Put the underlined words in the correct place.

Conversation 1

Excuse *tell*

A: Thank me, can you library me where the library is?

B: The ¹reception?

A: Yes, that's right.

B: It's next to the main ²excuse.

A: ³kind you.

B: I can take you there if you like.

A: That's very ⁴tell.

Conversation 2

A: Do you ⁵opens if the cafeteria is open?

B: ⁶Thank?

A: Is the ⁷know open now?

B: Yes. I think it ⁸cafeteria at 8.30a.m.

A: ⁹Sorry you.

Conversation 3

A: Excuse me. Could you ¹⁰classroom me?

B: Yes.

A: Can you ¹¹help me where my classroom is?

B: Have you got your registration form?

A: ¹²tell?

B: Your registration form. ¹³Thank I have your registration form?

A: Yes, ¹⁴Sorry it is.

B: Your ¹⁵Can is room 401. It's over there, near the bookshop.

A: ¹⁶here you.

LEARN TO check information

3A Complete the responses using the prompts in brackets.

1 A: It's next to the bookshop.
   B: *The bookshop* ? The one near the cafeteria? (repeat key word/phrase)
   A: That's right.

2 A: You can't bring your bag into the library.
   B: So, do I have to _____ here? (rephrase)
   A: That's right.

3 A: The exam starts at 9 o'clock.
   B: Did _____? (ask a checking question)
   A: That's right.

4 A: I need to buy a notebook.
   B: _____? There's a stationery shop over there. (repeat key word/phrase)
   A: Thank you.

5 A: Can you tell me where the study centre is?
   B: It's on the left as you go out of the building.
   A: _____? (ask for repetition)
   B: It's on the left as you go out of the building.
   A: Thank you.

6 A: Where can I find Professor Adams?
   B: He's in the lecture theatre.
   A: Did _____? (ask a checking question)
   B: Yes, he's giving a presentation.

B ▶ 7.4 Listen and check.

VOCABULARY money

1 Put the underlined letters in the correct order to complete the sentences.

1 I'm going to pay by <u>rdtcie</u> <u>radc</u> *credit card* .

2 I decided to pay by <u>hasc</u> _____.

3 Can you <u>eldn</u> _____ me some money?

4 Who's going to pay the <u>libl</u> _____ for this meal?

5 I usually <u>woorbr</u> _____ books from the library.

6 In my country, the <u>tosen</u> _____ are green or brown and have pictures of our presidents.

7 I want a drink. Do you have any <u>iosnc</u> _____ for this machine?

8 Do you usually <u>itp</u> _____ taxi drivers in your country?

9 Lawyers <u>rane</u> _____ a lot of money.

10 She decided to <u>nvites</u> _____ her money in a small printing business.

11 How much is this painting <u>tohrw</u> _____?

MONEY TAKERS - BIG FAILURES

Steven Panjani was robbing a bank, but he needed a bag for the money. He emptied his sports bag and put the money in it. Unfortunately, he left several things in the bank, including his wallet, a bank [1]_____, a [2]_____ from the same bank, an electricity [3]_____ and his house keys. He left these on the floor of the bank and was arrested twenty minutes later.

A woman in Sri Lanka went to a company and said she wanted to [4]_____ some money in it. Then she gave them a fake $1 million [5]_____. These don't exist! The manager called the police.

A child robbed a sweet shop.

He got a bag full of [6]_____, but he dropped them. He spent five minutes trying to pick them up and finished at the same time as the police arrived.

A customer at a restaurant gave the waiter his coat, but left his wallet in it. Later the waiter, Emilio Delgado, was found with $400 in [7]_____ from the wallet. When arrested, Delgado said 'It's a [8]_____ from a customer! I [9]_____ it this afternoon!'

Willy Finn booked into a US hotel and paid by [10]_____. That night, he robbed the reception. The police looked at his registration, saw his name and address, went to his house and arrested him.

2 Circle the correct option to complete the text, a), b) or c).

1 a) cash   b) statement   c) coin
2 a) tip   b) cash   c) credit card
3 a) bill   b) cheque   c) tip
4 a) earn   b) lend   c) invest
5 a) note   b) credit card   c) ATM
6 a) receipt   b) ATMs   c) coins
7 a) cash   b) statement   c) bill
8 a) cheque   b) tip   c) coin
9 a) lent   b) earned   c) invested in
10 a) tip   b) receipt   c) cheque

GRAMMAR relative clauses

3 Use relative clauses to make one sentence from the two sentences below.

1 Callin is a private university. I studied physics there.

   Callin is the private university *where I studied physics* .

2 Renata Samuels is a dentist. She fixed my teeth.

   Renata Samuels is the dentist _____.

3 La Cosecha is a bar. You get free food there.

   La Cosecha is a bar _____.

4 Did you get my note? I left it on your table.

   Did you get the note _____?

5 Mannix Music is a shop. It sells old CDs.

   Mannix Music is the shop _____.

6 Did you find the keys? I gave them to your girlfriend.

   Did you find the keys _____?

7 David Bynes is a personal trainer. He helped me get fit.

   David Bynes is the personal trainer _____.

8 Konstanz is a town. I was born there.

   Konstanz is the town _____.

9 This is the person. He introduced me to your sister.

   This is the person _____.

4 Find and correct the mistakes. There are mistakes in seven of the sentences.

1 Are these the photos /~~who~~ you were
      that
   looking for?

2 It's a place which you can really relax.

3 Do you still see your friend who she became a motorcycle courier?

4 Clarissa started a company that it sells organic food.

5 The book is about a girl who finds a magic forest.

6 That's the house that I was born.

7 I don't like people which talk all the time.

8 What's the name of the cake that we ate yesterday?

9 Is this the iPod that you want it?

READING

5A Which of the people in the pictures do you think earns the most money per hour? Read the text to find out.

David Beckham

J K Rowling

Nicole Kidman

THE REAL MONEY MAKERS

1 When English football team Arsenal bought a Japanese player called Junichi Inamoto, the team's fans gave him a nickname: 'T-shirt'. Why? Because they thought the club bought him so that they could sell more Arsenal T-shirts in Japan. Inamoto was a very good player, but he played only five games in a year at Arsenal, none of them important. His name and face did, however, sell a lot of T-shirts.

2 These days, sportspeople around the world can make lots of money without even playing. When David Beckham went to a USA team, LA Galaxy, in 2007, he made £500,000 a week. That's nearly £3,000 an hour. Michael Ballack, a German footballer who plays for Chelsea, in London, makes £130,000 a week. If he plays in two games per week, that equals £43,300 per hour of playing.

3 Of course it's not only football players who can make big money by the minute. Back in 1978, actor Marlon Brando played the role of Superman's father in the film *Superman*. He appeared for less than fifteen minutes in the film and didn't learn his lines. These had to be written on various pieces of paper around the film set! For this he earned $3.7 million. In 2004, Nicole Kidman made $2 million for a three-minute advertisement for the perfume Chanel No. 5. The company said it was a short film, a piece of art, not just an advertisement.

4 So who else makes big money in a short time? Of course there is Bill Gates and the usual businesspeople: the Walton family, who own Wal-Mart; Mexican telephone billionaire Carlos Slim Helu and Howard Stern, a US radio DJ who makes about £311 a minute. And who is the biggest money maker in literature? J K Rowling, author of the Harry Potter books. She makes about £100,000 a day. Now that is magic!

B Read the text again and answer the questions.
Who:

1 helped a football team to sell T-shirts?
_____

2 made over a million dollars for every five minutes of a film? _____

3 employed an actress to sell perfume? _____

4 writes books that earn her £100,000 a day? _____

C Find words in the text to match definitions 1–5.

1 people who like a team and want them to win (paragraph 1) _____

2 a short or friendly name that is used by friends or family (paragraph 1) _____

3 the words that an actor learns for a play or a film (paragraph 3) _____

4 someone with $1,000,000,000, £1,000,000,000 or €1,000,000,000 (paragraph 4) _____

5 a special power that makes impossible things happen (paragraph 4) _____

WRITING adding emphasis

6A Read the product description and put the words in brackets in the correct places.

Hanser Lightman six-string acoustic guitar: €45

The guitar is in good condition. (very)

The previous owner used it for only two months, and it plays. (perfectly)

We can ship it to you – within 24 hours. (quickly)

This is a good offer for a beginner. (really)

The guitar is easy to play. (extremely)

B Write a product description of one of these products in 50–100 words.

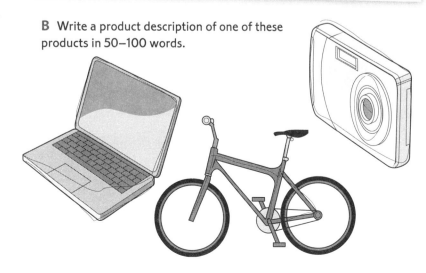

VOCABULARY multi-word verbs

1 Read the blog entries and underline the correct alternative.

BLAMESOMEONEELSE.COM

My wife wanted a new sofa. We bought the biggest, most expensive sofa in the shop, but it ¹*took over/took up/took in* too much space in the living room. After two weeks, we ²*took it up/took it in/took it back*. Bigger isn't always better.

Chad

I borrowed €800 two months ago from a rich friend, who forgot about it. I really needed the money. My girlfriend told me to ³*give it over/give it back/give it in*. I didn't. She told me again and again. Eventually I ⁴*gave in/gave over/gave at*. I returned the money. Then I was poor, so she left me. Now she's going out with my rich friend.

Rick

We started a club for people who wanted to ⁵*give in/give round/give up* smoking. We spent our time watching films and playing games (no smoking allowed). I invited my friend, but after a few weeks, he ⁶*took up/took back/took over* the club. He loves playing cards. Now we play cards seven days a week. We're all addicted.

Lena

---

2 Complete the sentences below with the prepositions in the box.

> back (x2)   up (x2)   in   over

1 I played squash for twenty years until I gave it _____ last year.
2 Every day she asked me for an iPod. Eventually I gave _____ and bought her one for Christmas.
3 When are you going to give _____ that book you borrowed from me?
4 This desk takes _____ too much space.
5 We expected things to change after we took _____ the company.
6 This computer doesn't work so I'm taking it _____ to the shop.

3 ▶ 8.1 Listen and repeat the phrases from Exercise 2. Concentrate on the stressed prepositions.

GRAMMAR *too much/many, enough, very*

4 Look at the pictures and the table. Complete the sentences with *too, much, many, enough* or *very* and say who each sentence is about.

MELANIE

SANDRA

DORIS

	food/drink	exercise	work	TV	sleep
Melanie	spends €150 a week	30 minutes a week	44 hours a week	40 hours a week	12 hours a night
Sandra	spends €80 a week	38 hours a week	40 hours a week	no TV	8 hours a night
Doris	spends €430 a week	5 hours a week	65 hours a week	7 hours a week	4 hours a night

1 She eats too __*much*__ junk food. __*Melanie*__
2 She doesn't do _____ exercise. _____
3 She does too _____ exercise. _____
4 She doesn't sleep _____. _____
5 She sleeps _____ much. _____
6 She is _____ unhealthy. _____
7 She works too _____ hours a week. _____
8 She watches too _____ TV. _____
9 She eats _____ different types of vegetable. _____
10 She spends _____ much money on food. _____

5 Match sentence beginnings a)–b) with endings i)–ii).

1 a) There isn't enough food here; ____
  b) There's too much food here; ____

  i) we won't need all of it.
  ii) we need to buy some more.

2 a) He's too good at tennis ____
  b) He's very good at tennis ____

  i) and I love watching him play.
  ii) for us – the game will be boring if he plays.

3 a) There are too many ____
  b) There's too much ____

  i) traffic on the roads.
  ii) cars on the roads.

4 a) This film is too ____
  b) In this film there is too ____

  i) long.
  ii) much violence.

5 a) We don't have much time to catch the bus, ____
  b) We don't have enough time to catch the bus, ____

  i) so we have to be quick.
  ii) so we'll take a taxi.

6 a) The homework was very difficult ____
  b) The homework was too difficult ____

  i) so I didn't finish it.
  ii) but I finished it.

7 a) Oh no! I've been out in the sun too long ____
  b) I've had enough sun ____

  i) and I'm burnt now.
  ii) so I'm going inside.

8 a) I spent too much ____
  b) I spent too many ____

  i) time relaxing, so I failed my course.
  ii) days away from my work, so I lost my job.

LISTENING

6A ▶ 8.2 Look at pictures 1–6, which show a true story. What do you think happened? Listen and check.

B Find and correct the mistakes. There are five mistakes in the summary of the story below. The first one has been done for you.

Maggie and Joe Smith lived in the same house for ~~fifteen~~ *fifty* years. When Joe died, Maggie sold the house to David Jones. A few years later, Maggie heard someone say that Jones had found some money in her old house. Jones told her there was $10,000 in the wall. He offered her $5,000. She agreed. A few days later, Jones asked Maggie to sign a contract that said she should accept $5,000 for any money found in the garden. She didn't sign it. Instead, she took Jones to court. In court, he told the truth: there wasn't $10,000. There was $15,000. Joe Smith, Maggie's husband, was putting money in the wall for fifty years and he never told his wife. In the end, the judge decided that Mr Jones should get all of the money.

VOCABULARY shopping

1 Use the clues to complete the puzzle and find the hidden word.

1 a person who uses a service or buys something from a shop

2 paper or material attached to a product with information about the product on it

3 the particular type/name of a product (sometimes famous, e.g., Levi Jeans, Ferrari cars)

4 a big shop where you can buy many things, especially food

5 when you buy things on the computer, you shop …

6 this person sells meat

FUNCTION buying things

2 Put the words in the correct order to make conversations.

1 A: I / you / help / can ?

B: looking, / just / I'm / thanks

2 A: particular / looking / you / anything / in / are / for ?

B: hats / you / do / sell ?

3 A: these / you / larger / one / size / in / do / a / have / of ?

B: just / look / I'll / have / a

4 A: I / on / these / try / can ?

B: here / yes, / the / is / room / fitting

5 A: card / you / cash / are / by / credit / or / paying ?

B: card / credit / by

6 A: you / PIN / your / enter / can ?

B: of / yes, / course

3 Complete the text with one word in each gap.

‘ When I started in 1948, everything was different. Everyone paid by [1]_____ because credit cards didn't exist. Now you have to ask them to enter their [2]_____ or [3]_____ their name. Shops were much smaller in those days too. If a customer was looking for something in [4]_____, like a dress in a special colour, or if the shoes didn't [5]_____ and they needed a smaller [6]_____, we made it for them. And people didn't really go window shopping. You never heard people say 'I'm just [7]_____,' because people only went to shops if they wanted to buy something. In the smaller shops, you knew most of your customers. These days, the first thing you say is [8]'_____ I help you?' In those days it was, 'Hello, John. How are you?' ’

LEARN TO describe things

4 Underline the correct alternative.

1 A: Excuse me. I'm looking for one of those *stuff/things* you use to open cans.

B: You mean a can opener. They're just over there.

2 A: Excuse me. Do you have any of that *stuff/things* for taking paint off walls?

B: You mean paint stripper? We have some just here.

3 A: I'm looking for fusilli. It's *type/a type* of pasta.

B: Oh, I'm afraid we're out of stock.

4 A: Hello. Do you have any books by Malcolm Gladwell? He's *kind a/a kind of* journalist.

B: Oh yes. They're in the popular psychology section.

LISTENING

5A ▶ 8.3 Listen and match pictures A–D with conversations 1–4.

B Listen again and answer the questions.

1 In conversation 1, what does the customer want? _____

2 In conversation 2, what two things does the sales assistant show the customer? _____ _____

3 In conversation 3, does the sales assistant find what he's looking for? _____

4 In conversation 4, how does the customer pay? _____

VOCABULARY nature

1 Circle the correct option to complete the sentences.

1 The Pacific and the Arctic are both _____.

  a) seas   b) oceans

2 The Atacama and the Gobi are both _____.

  a) mountains   b) deserts

3 The Himalayas and the Alps are both _____.

  a) mountain ranges   b) lakes

4 The Nile and the Mississippi are both _____.

  a) seas   b) rivers

5 Victoria and Superior are two of the world's largest _____.

  a) rivers   b) lakes

6 Iguaçu and Niagara are two of the world's largest _____.

  a) waterfalls   b) rainforests

GRAMMAR comparatives/superlatives

2 Look at the table below and make sentences comparing France and Poland using the word in brackets.

	France	Poland
Population	60 million people	38 million people
Size	548,000 square km	313,000 square km
Highest mountain	4,810 m (Mont Blanc)	2,499 m (Rysy)
Average temperature (January)	3 °C	−3 °C
Average temperature (July)	23 °C	19 °C

1 The population in France is ... the population in Poland. (big)

  The population in France is bigger than the population
  in Poland.

2 Poland is ... France. (small)

  _____

3 Mont Blanc, in France, is ... Rysy in Poland. (high)

  _____

4 In January, it is ... than in France. (cold)

  _____

5 In July, it is ... than in Poland. (hot)

  _____

3A ▶ 9.1 Listen to the comparative phrases. Circle the correct stress pattern.

a) oOo   b) Ooo   c) ooO

B Listen again and repeat the phrases.

C ▶ 9.2 Listen and check the answers to Exercise 2. Then listen and repeat.

4 Make sentences using the comparative/superlative forms of the words in brackets.

1 It's been _____ (cold) winter in thirty years.

2 The weather is getting _____ (bad).

3 It's _____ (popular) tourist destination in the country.

4 It's _____ (cheap) to stay in a bed and breakfast than to stay in a hotel.

5 People are working _____ (long) hours than before.

6 The summers are much _____ (hot) than they were.

7 In the winter, the days are _____ (short).

8 This sauce tastes _____ (good) than the other one you made.

9 We've been on _____ (long) journey of our lives.

10 Yesterday I felt bad, but today I'm much _____ (happy).

11 It's _____ (funny) programme I've ever watched.

12 The exam was _____ (difficult) than I expected.

READING

5 Look at the reasons 1–4 for growing your own vegetables. Then read the text. Which reasons are mentioned?

1 'It's a good way to relax.'

2 'The food tastes better when you grow it yourself.'

3 'It's cheaper than buying food in the supermarket.'

4 'It's a good way to earn some extra money.'

MAKING THE WORLD A GREENER PLACE: GROW YOUR OWN VEGETABLES

We meet people from around the world who enjoy growing their own food.

United States
When you think of Washington, you might not think of vegetable patches, but there are lots of them. 'Community plots' where people can grow their own food are getting more popular. Brian Wallis, who works in banking, likes gardening in his free time. And he's not alone. 'When you work in the city, gardening is a great way to relax,' he says.

Australia
Outside Sydney, there are more than fifty community gardens. In the garden at the Addison Road Centre, people grow all kinds of things, from bananas to coffee, herbs, beans and vegetables. They also have lemon, peach and cherry trees. People come here to learn new skills related to organic gardening and recycling.

Kenya
In Kenya, having a piece of land to grow food on is not just a good way to relax, it's a way to earn some extra money. Maxwell shares the land his father gave him with his six brothers. They grow bananas, coffee and sugar on the land, as well as vegetables to eat at home. 'Some of the food we eat ourselves,' he says, 'and some we sell at the market.'

Russia
Every weekend in the summer, the roads of Russia's big cities are full of traffic, with families escaping to their 'dacha'. A 'dacha' can be anything from an old shed in a field to a huge house in the countryside, but the reason they go is the same. People from the city can enjoy the clean air and grow some vegetables. Tatiana, who has a plot near the Black Sea, grows tomatoes and cucumbers in the summer and cabbages in the winter. 'It always tastes much better when you grow it yourself,' she says.

6 Read the text again and answer the questions.

1 Why does Brian Wallis think people enjoy gardening?

_____

_____

2 What can people learn at the Addison Road Centre, outside Sydney?

_____

_____

3 How did Maxwell get his land?

_____

_____

4 What does Maxwell do with the food they grow?

_____

_____

5 What is a 'dacha' in Russia?

_____

_____

6 What can people who live in Russian cities enjoy at their 'dacha'?

_____

_____

WRITING similar sounding words

7 Find and correct the mistakes. There is a spelling mistake in each sentence.

1 Is this you're coat?

2 They gave us there car for the weekend.

3 Have you got an extra ticket? I'd like to come to.

4 We spent the weekend by the see.

5 Do you know wear the office is?

6 Are you sure this is the write way?

8 Underline the correct alternative to complete the text.

How often do you use ¹*you're/your* car? I try to use the car as little as possible. I walk or use my bike to get around. I live in a small city though, so ²*it's/its* quite easy. And it keeps me fit ³*two/to/too*. If I want to go to the ⁴*see/sea* for the weekend, or something like that, then I usually get the bus or the train. I don't think people should spend so much time in ⁵*there/their* cars. It's not ⁶*write/right*.

VOCABULARY the outdoors

1A Find seven more words connected with the outdoors in the word square.

F	E	A	T	U	R	E	S	C
N	D	E	R	F	S	G	C	O
A	I	R	O	Y	Z	A	E	R
T	S	T	P	A	R	K	N	U
U	D	E	I	F	C	X	E	R
R	S	F	C	O	P	L	R	A
A	D	N	A	M	E	W	Y	L
L	W	I	L	D	L	I	F	E

B Use words from the word square to complete phrases 1–8.

1 geographical _____
2 fresh _____
3 national _____
4 beautiful _____
5 _____ centre
6 _____ rainforest
7 _____ area
8 _____ beauty

C Complete the sentences using the phrases from B.

1 We live in a polluted city, but in the countryside near us you can breathe _____ _____.
2 I hate cities. I prefer living in a _____ _____ because I grew up on a farm.
3 Unfortunately, the _____ _____ was closed so we didn't see the rare birds.
4 Mountains, waterfalls and volcanoes are examples of _____ _____ you can find on this continent.
5 The Amazon is the world's biggest _____ _____; it has incredible plant life because of all the rain.
6 Our biggest _____ _____ is Etosha. You can drive around it and see wild animals.
7 We went for a walk in the hills. Then we stopped to take photos of the _____ _____.
8 The Cotswolds is an area of _____ _____. It's very green.

GRAMMAR articles

2 Complete the sentences with the words in the box and add *a*, *an*, *the* or – (no article).

right January doctor weather Europe architect camera elephants noise Thursday sun

1 My house is on ___the right___.
2 It's so cold in Iceland. I really hate _____.
3 During our safari in Namibia we saw _____.
4 He loved buildings and wanted to be _____.
5 I bought a camera and a bag. Then we went travelling, and I dropped and broke _____.
6 When I was twenty, I travelled around _____.
7 I'm working in December, but I'll be on holiday in _____.
8 Let me see him! I can help. I'm _____.
9 We didn't have a map to guide us, so we used _____.
10 See you on _____.
11 I heard a small noise. After a while, _____ got louder.

3 Complete the book review with *a*, *an*, *the* or – (no article).

A WALK ON THE WILD SIDE BY GIUSEPPE DE LUCA (TRANS. OLIVIA CARSON)

Giuseppe de Luca has been [1] *an* adventurer all his life. He once ran away from home in [2] ___ Sicily and survived on fish that he caught from [3] ___ river with his hands. De Luca's book explains why he can't do [4] ___ normal job. He has tried office work, building boats, driving lorries across Europe and looking for dinosaur bones in [5] ___ Kenya. He couldn't do any of these for more than [6] ___ few months. He finally finds happiness living on [7] ___ smallest beach in Papua New Guinea. But then he has some [8] ___ problems with the local police, and they send him back to Sicily. Why is his story so interesting? It's his humour and his innocence. He is shy with girls. He doesn't have [9] ___ email address and he has never touched [10] ___ mobile phone. He clearly loves living alone in [11] ___ wild and his book makes a great companion.

LISTENING

4A ▶ 9.3 Listen and match speakers 1–4 with statements a)–d).

a) He/She has spent a lot of time in the garden. ____

b) He/She lives on a farm. ____

c) He/She lives near a beach. ____

d) He/She comes from the USA. ____

B Listen again and answer the questions in three words or fewer.

1 a) What does she do on the beach these days?

_____

b) What did she see on the beach once?

_____

2 a) What names did she know?

_____

b) Where does she say she 'grew up'?

_____

3 a) When does he go hiking and camping?

_____

b) What 'big' things does he say that Americans like?

_____

4 a) What animals does he work with?

_____

b) What doesn't he like about living on a farm?

_____

C Match the words and phrases in bold in 1–8 with meanings a)–h).

1 That was **fun**. ____

2 It was **enormous**. ____

3 I played in a **tree house**. ____

4 You could **be outside** all day. ____

5 I go **hiking**. ____

6 There are **all kinds of** plants and animals. ____

7 It's **completely normal** to see animals around. ____

8 I really like **feeding** the pigs. ____

a) walking for a long time in the countryside

b) very common

c) giving food to someone/something

d) enjoyable

e) many different types of

f) a small house in a tree (usually for children)

g) extremely big

h) be in the open air, not in a building

D Read what Gyorgi says about his experiences in nature. Complete the text with the words and phrases from Exercise C.

'When I was younger, I lived in a very cold part of Russia. It was ¹_____ for the temperature to be minus twenty degrees, and in the winter, you might not ²_____ for many weeks. We spent a lot of time at home playing games and singing in front of the fire. To be honest, it wasn't much ³_____ in winter, but in the summer we did ⁴_____ enjoyable activities. Where I lived, there were some mountains and forests, and we sometimes went ⁵_____ in the mountains with my parents. And I remember we once built a ⁶_____ in my garden. My brother loved birds and he spent hours ⁷_____ them different types of fruit and nuts while he was sitting in that tree house. As a child I always thought our garden was ⁸_____, but when I went back there a few years ago, I saw that it was quite small.'

VOCABULARY animals

1 Name the animals 1–10 to complete the puzzle and find the hidden word.

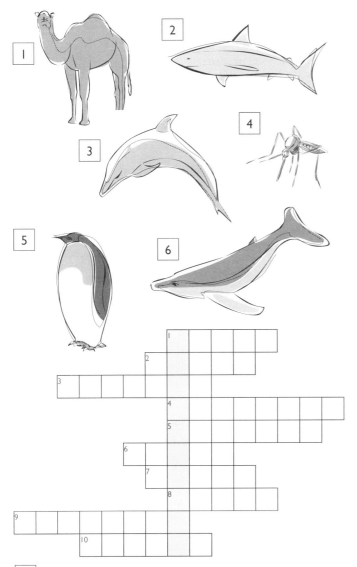

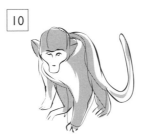

FUNCTION making guesses

2 Find and correct the mistakes. There are mistakes in five of the sentences.

1 That animal might to be a chimpanzee or a monkey.
2 Maybe that's a glacier in the photo.
3 The waterfall don't can be here – it's too dry.
4 That bird can't be an eagle – it's too small.
5 They must be have a dog – look at all the hair on the sofa!
6 The mountain range in the picture could to be the Himalayas.
7 Those might be a bear's footprints on the ground.
8 That's definitely no a mosquito bite – it's too big.

3 Underline the correct alternatives to complete the paragraphs.

1 The rain forest is home to 30 percent of all animal and plant life on Earth and 2.5 million types of insects. But it is disappearing because people cut down the trees for money. We don't know how fast it is disappearing, but satellite pictures show that it *might/definitely* be 15,000 km every year. Some scientists think the rain forest *could/can't* disappear completely by 2080.

2 We aren't sure exactly how many people died during the tsunami of 2004, but it was *might/perhaps* as many as 230,000. The tsunami destroyed large parts of Indonesia, Sri Lanka, India and Thailand, and the complete reconstruction of houses and other buildings *can't/might* take ten years or more.

3 Everyone knows Venice – it *can't/must* be the world's most famous city built on water – but now it has a big problem: it is sinking into the water. The situation is very serious: *maybe/could* Venice will be completely under water in forty years.

4 Because of global warming, the ice is melting in the Arctic and some scientists say there *must/might* be no ice there by 2060. Many animals that live in the Arctic, for example polar bears and foxes, *could/perhaps* be in danger.

LEARN TO give yourself time to think

4 Put the underlined letters in the correct order to complete the conversations.

1 A: Are you coming to the party tonight?
   B: <u>lelw</u> _____, I hope so. But I have a lot of homework to do.
2 A: How do you stop this machine?
   B: <u>ahtt's a odgo eisunotq</u> _____. Perhaps it's that button there.
3 A: Who do you think is going to win?
   B: <u>ti's dhra ot yas</u> _____. But Manchester United are a great team.
4 A: Where were you yesterday at 4.00?
   B: <u>tel em ntkih</u> _____. I was at home!
5 A: How old is Lina?
   B: <u>ml' tno eurs</u> _____. Maybe thirty? Or thirty-five?

GRAMMAR *used to*

1 **Complete the sentences using *used to*. Write two words.**

1 I went to the cinema every week when I was a student. Now I hardly ever go.

 I used to go to the cinema a lot.

2 William paints every day. He never did this before.

 William _____ _____ to paint every day.

3 I drank fizzy drinks all the time when I was younger. Now I never drink them.

 I used _____ _____ fizzy drinks.

4 These days she reads a lot. In the past she read very little.

 She didn't _____ _____ read much.

5 I recognise that woman. Did she live near us?

 Did _____ _____ to live near us?

6 When I was young, I played the guitar, violin, drums and flute. Now I don't play anything.

 I used _____ _____ lots of musical instruments.

7 I remember your cousins. Did they visit you regularly years ago?

 _____ _____ cousins use to stay with you?

8 My father always called me Princess when I was a child. Now he calls me by my real name.

 My father _____ _____ call me Princess.

9 I hated classical music when I was a teenager. Now I love it.

 I didn't _____ _____ like classical music.

10 When I was younger I was a teacher. Now I am a tour guide.

 I used _____ _____ a teacher.

GRAMMAR purpose, cause and result

2 **Complete the sentences with *so*, *to* or *because*.**

1 Sarah was unhappy *because* I forgot her birthday.

2 I ate the bread _____ I was hungry.

3 The tickets were too expensive _____ we didn't go to the concert.

4 Yuko was ill _____ she didn't come to class.

5 Ben went to Liberia _____ make a documentary.

6 She was unhealthy _____ she smoked and ate fatty foods.

7 I bought a money belt _____ keep my passport and cash safe.

8 It was really hot _____ Pilar wore her sunhat.

9 They are here _____ take an exam.

10 I went to the shops _____ buy some milk.

11 Sandra was cold and tired _____ she went home.

12 Jacob didn't buy anything _____ he didn't have any money.

FUNCTION finding out information

3A **Write out the sentences in full.**

1 Cld u hlp me? _____

2 Cn u tll me whr th offc is? _____

3 Whr cn I fnd a pst offc? _____

4 Wht tm ds th lbrry opn? _____

5 Whn do th lssns strt? _____

6 Is th swmmng pl opn on Sndys? _____

7 I nd t spk t th director of studies. _____

B ▶ RC3.1 **Listen and check.**

VOCABULARY revision

4 **Complete the conversations with the words in the box.**

about documentary cure moves for spent lecture back travel desk room with

1 A: I'm thinking _about_ becoming a doctor.

 B: So you can _____ people?

2 A: I _____ a year abroad after university. I went to Spain, Italy and Poland.

 B: That sounds great! I'd love to _____ around Europe.

3 A: Oh no! I left my book in the photocopying _____.

 B: You'll have to go _____ and get it.

4 A: Excuse me. Where's the registration _____?

 B: I don't know. I'm also looking _____ it!

5 A: I hear that film director is making a _____.

 B: Yes. It's about a British woman who _____ to the Amazon rain forest.

6 A: I'm so bored _____ my course!

 B: I know. I saw you sleeping in the _____ theatre!

GRAMMAR relative clauses

5 **Complete sentences 1–6 with the phrases in the box. Use relative clauses.**

builds his own hospital in India we drove to California you work quietly or borrow books was working as a model my son was born designs computer systems for businesses

1 The programme is about a Swiss doctor _who builds his own hospital in India_.

2 That's the car _____.

3 France is the country _____.

4 I work for an IT company _____.

5 Have you seen that friend of yours _____?

6 A library is a place _____.

GRAMMAR *too much/many, enough, very*

6 **Underline the correct alternative to complete the conversations.**

1 **A:** Do we have enough rice?
   B: Enough? We have far too *many/much/very*!

2 **A:** Do you want some more to eat?
   B: No thanks. I've eaten *much/many/enough*.

3 **A:** What do you think of this photographer?
   B: I think she's *much/enough/very* good.

4 **A:** Do you like your new house?
   B: Not really. It's *too/much/many* small for six people.

5 **A:** Are you enjoying life in the city?
   B: It's OK, but we don't have *much/very/many* friends.

6 **A:** Shall we study here?
   B: No. There's too *many/much/very* noise.

7 **A:** Do you want to buy this digital camera?
   B: I'd like to, but I don't have *many/too/enough* money.

FUNCTION buying things

7A **Find and correct the mistakes. There is a mistake in each sentence.**

1 Excuse me. Do you to sell binoculars?
2 Do you have one these in a larger size?
3 Are you looking for anything in particularly?
4 It isn't fitting me.
5 Are you paying by cash or the credit card?
6 Can you just to sign here, please?
7 Where's the fit room?

B **Who says the sentences: the customer (C) or the sales assistant (S)?**

VOCABULARY money; multi-word verbs; shopping

8 **Underline the correct answer.**

1 Which means give money to someone for a short time: *lend* or *borrow*?
2 Which is made of paper: *notes* or *coins*?
3 Which means you put money in a company: *invest in* or *earn*?
4 Which do you do when you buy a company: *take over* or *take in*?
5 Which means you stop doing something: *give back* or *give up*?
6 Which can be outside on the street: *supermarket* or *market*?
7 Which helps you if you have a problem when you are shopping: *customer service* or *brand*?

GRAMMAR comparatives/superlatives

9 **Put the words in the correct order to make sentences.**

1 elephants / lions / are / than / bigger
_____

2 gold / more / silver / than / expensive / is
_____

3 this / years / is / for / weather / worst / the / many
_____

4 Russia / world / biggest / the / in / is / the / country
_____

5 a / than / more / Mercedes / Toyota / expensive / is / a
_____

6 it's / I've / seen / film / the / ever / exciting / most
_____

GRAMMAR articles

10 **Complete the text with *a, an, the* or – (no article).**

¹ _A_ plane carrying ² ___ actor, ³ ___ politician, a monk and a cleaner is going to crash. There are only ⁴ ___ three parachutes. ⁵ ___ actor says, 'I entertain ⁶ ___ millions of people so I should live.' He takes one of ⁷ ___ parachutes and jumps out of ⁸ ___ plane. The politician says, 'I am ⁹ ___ most intelligent person in ¹⁰ ___ England so I should live.' He also takes ¹¹ ___ parachute and jumps. The monk says, 'I am ¹² ___ old man and I have lived ¹³ ___ good long life. You take ¹⁴ ___ last parachute.' The cleaner says, 'Don't worry. The most intelligent man in ¹⁵ ___ country just jumped out with my ¹⁶ ___ rucksack on his back.'

FUNCTION making guesses

11 **Cross out the alternative that is not possible in each conversation.**

1 **A:** Is that Richard in the photo?
   B: He has the same hair colour, but I'm not sure. It *could be/~~must be~~/might be*.

2 **A:** Are you going to the meeting tomorrow?
   B: I don't really know. *Maybe/I definitely will/Perhaps*.

3 **A:** What's the answer to question 3?
   B: I don't know, but *it can't be/it's definitely not/it must be* c because Moscow is in Russia.

4 **A:** Is Paris as expensive as London?
   B: It *could/can't/might* be. When I went there a few years ago, I paid €10 for a coffee!

5 **A:** Why hasn't she moved to a place nearer work?
   B: I don't know, but *it can't be/perhaps it's/it might be* too expensive.

VOCABULARY natural places; the outdoors; animals

12 **Put the words in the box into the correct category.**

> whale   monkey   fresh air   ocean   pigeon   dolphin   coastline
> eagle   geographical features   cheetah   wildlife centre   mosquito
> lake   bear   shark

natural places/ the outdoors	land animals	animals that fly	animals that live in water

TEST

Circle the correct option to complete the sentences.

1 I _____ to live in Valladolid in Spain.

   a) was   b) use   c) used

2 She didn't _____ to smoke.

   a) used   b) regularly   c) use

3 Who did you _____ to play with when you were a child?

   a) use   b) using   c) used

4 I studied for six years _____ become a doctor.

   a) so   b) to   c) for

5 I borrowed some money _____ I wanted to buy a car.

   a) because   b) for   c) so

6 The lecture was boring _____ we left early.

   a) therefore   b) why   c) so

7 Where _____ I find a bookshop?

   a) can   b) must   c) does

8 _____ you tell me where the housing office is?

   a) Shall   b) Could   c) Do

9 One day, I'm going to travel _____ the world.

   a) everywhere   b) on   c) around

10 He wanted to _____ famous.

   a) become   b) make   c) have

11 This is the shop _____ I worked for ten years.

   a) that   b) what   c) where

12 She's the woman _____ gave me a $50 tip last week.

   a) which   b) who   c) how

13 This is the restaurant _____ serves terrible frozen food.

   a) who   b) what   c) that

14 I don't do _____ exercise.

   a) a lot   b) enough   c) too

15 There are still some trams in San Francisco, but not _____.

   a) much   b) very   c) many

16 My bag is full because I bought _____ many souvenirs.

   a) too   b) enough   c) very

17 Can I try _____ these jeans?

   a) on   b) in   c) up

18 This shirt doesn't _____.

   a) fitted   b) right   c) fit

19 Can you _____ me some money?

   a) do   b) lend   c) borrow

20 She gave _____ eating meat last year.

   a) up   b) out   c) back

21 That was the _____ meal I've ever eaten.

   a) good   b) best   c) better

22 That cinema is _____ away than this one.

   a) father   b) far   c) further

23 Your boat is _____ beautiful than ours.

   a) the   b) most   c) more

24 At a party yesterday I met _____ man who knows you.

   a) – (no article)   b) a   c) the

25 My dog is always barking at _____ moon.

   a) a   b) – (no article)   c) the

26 She's _____ best player in the team.

   a) the   b) a   c) most

27 We _____ go to Spain this summer, but we aren't sure.

   a) definitely   b) might   c) maybe

28 The answer isn't a or b so it _____ be c.

   a) can't   b) perhaps   c) must

29 It's one of the biggest mountain _____ in the world.

   a) lines   b) places   c) ranges

30 I used to live in a _____ area, far from the city.

   a) rural   b) wildlife   c) park

TEST RESULT /30

VOCABULARY describing a city

1 Add vowels to complete the words and phrases.

1 There's a lot of tr__ff__c.
2 It's very cr__wd__d.
3 The streets are cl____n and s__f__.
4 I love the n__ghtl__f__.
5 There are lots of th__ngs t__ s____ and d__.
6 The p__bl__c tr__nsp__rt syst__m is excellent.
7 In the city centre, there's quite a lot of cr__me.
8 I usually find people are fr____ndly and p__l__t__.
9 There are some lovely parks and gr____n sp__c__s.
10 Some of the old b____ld__ngs are beautiful.

2 Complete people's opinions about where they live. Use the phrases in brackets to help you.

1 'There are lots of beautiful _____, like the museums and the cathedral.' (places like houses, with walls and a roof)
2 'The _____ _____ system is great. It's really cheap.' (buses, trams and underground)
3 'It's a problem in the morning, because there's a lot of _____.' (a lot of cars)
4 'People are always very _____ and _____.' (stop to talk or help you, say things like 'please' and 'thank you')
5 'The thing I like best is the parks. There are lots of _____ _____ where you can go for a walk or sit and enjoy the view.' (places with trees and plants)
6 'The problem is that there's a lot of _____.' (illegal activity)
7 'It's an industrial city, so it's very _____.' (air and water are not clean)
8 'I don't like going into the city, because it's very _____.' (too many people in a small space)
9 'It has a great _____ with lots of clubs staying open all night long.' (places to go out at night)
10 'I like it where I live. The streets are _____ and _____.' (no rubbish or crime)

GRAMMAR uses of like

3 Complete the conversations using phrases with like.

1 A: Did you choose the salmon starter? What's _____?
   B: It's delicious. Try some.
2 A: Do _____ classical music?
   B: No, I can't stand it. I only listen to rock.
3 A: What _____ doing at the weekend?
   B: Nothing much. We like staying at home and relaxing!
4 A: What was your weekend _____?
   B: It was great. We went out on Saturday and had a really good time.
5 A: I haven't met your sister. What's _____?
   B: She's really funny. I'm sure you'll like her.
6 A: _____ the weather _____ at the moment?
   B: It's raining, as usual.
7 A: _____ living in London?
   B: I love it. There are so many things to see and do.
8 A: What _____ that new restaurant by the river _____?
   B: It's lovely. We ate there last week.

4A There is a mistake in each question. Add, cut or change a word to correct the mistakes.

1 A: What's your new ~~be~~ teacher like?
   B: She's really good. She makes the lessons interesting.
2 A: What's it to like living in the country?
   B: It's a bit quiet. I think I preferred the city.
3 A: Does your mother staying with you?
   B: She loves it. She comes to stay once a month.
4 A: Are you like eating out in restaurants?
   B: I enjoy it sometimes, but I prefer to cook at home.
5 A: Is it much more expensive to live there now? What the prices like?
   B: It's not too bad. But it's more expensive than it was.
6 A: Do your brother like it in Scotland?
   B: He likes it a lot. He says it's beautiful.
7 A: Which's your new job like? Are you enjoying it?
   B: It's brilliant. The people I work with are really friendly.

B ▶ 10.1 **Listen and check.**

C ▶ 10.2 **Listen and repeat the questions.**

Where is the city of love?

Which is the most romantic city in the world? Which is the cheapest? We've travelled around the world to find the cheapest, most romantic and safest cities. Can you find your perfect destination?

The world's most romantic city

1 Paris is the city of love. Most Europeans think Paris is the most romantic city in Europe, although Vienna, Prague and Venice are popular too. So what's the most romantic thing you can do in Paris? Well it's not go to the top of the Eiffel tower – that's too crowded. Buy some bread and cheese and enjoy a picnic near the river. Or spend the afternoon sitting outside a pavement café, sipping champagne, laughing, and just watching the people go by. Paris is perfect for lovers.

The cheapest city in the world

2 Asunción is Paraguay's capital and has won the title of 'least expensive city in the world' five times. Every year there is a list made of the most expensive cities in the world to live in. They look at the prices of things like food, bills and public transport and cities like Moscow, London and Tokyo are always at the top. However, for five years Asunción has been number 143 on the list, giving it the title of the cheapest place in the world to live.

The safest city

3 Did you know that New York is now one of America's safest big cities? There is less crime now, and what was once one of the most dangerous cities in the world is not any more. This is good news for the 40 million visitors who come to New York every year for the great shopping, the museums, some of the best restaurants in the world, and of course to see the Statue of Liberty, Times Square and other famous sights.

READING

5 Write answers to the questions. Then read the article above to check your answers.

1 Which city is called 'the most romantic' by more than 50 percent of Europeans? _____

2 Which is the cheapest city to live in? _____

3 Which statement about New York is true?
  a) It is one of the safest big cities in the USA.
  b) It is one of the most dangerous cities in the USA.

6 Read the article again and answer the questions.

1 Do people think that Vienna is a romantic city?

2 What's the problem with going to the Eiffel Tower?

3 According to the article, are Moscow, London and Tokyo expensive cities to live in?

4 Are food and public transport expensive in Asunción?

5 Has New York always been a safe city?

6 What is special about the restaurants in New York?

7 Find words or phrases in the article to match definitions 1–6.

1 a meal that you eat outside away from home (paragraph 1): _____

2 walk past (paragraph 1): _____

3 the most important city in a country (where the government is) (paragraph 2): _____

4 the name of something/the name you win in a competition (paragraph 2): _____

5 was at one time (paragraph 3): _____

6 things that tourists visit in a city (paragraph 3): _____

WRITING using formal expressions

8 Put the words in the correct order to complete the letter.

1 Mr / Smith / dear

2 ask / college / am / courses / I / at / to / about / your / writing

_____

3 you / know / have / I'd / to / in / like / August / courses / what

_____

4 this / prices / addition / to / in / know / the / like / I / to / would

_____

5 soon / to / I / from / forward / you / look / hearing

_____

6 sincerely / Bridges / yours / Sally

_____

9 Write a letter (80–100 words) asking for information about the accommodation in the advertisement.

> Host family accommodation available for students. Please write to Sam Wellings for further details.
> Sam Wellings, Accommodation Officer
> 15 Leigh St.
> Oxford
> MK20 6UP

VOCABULARY crime and punishment

1 Complete the words in the sentences.

1 The pol _i_ ce off _i_ c _e_ r caught the th _i_ _e_ f.
2 The j __ dg __ gave her a long pr __ s __ n s __ nt __ nc __ .
3 A lot of sh __ pl __ ft __ rs st ___ l mobile phones.
4 The cr __ m __ n __ l knew the v __ ct __ m.
5 He was given a f __ n __ for wr __ t __ ng gr __ ff __ t __ on the wall of a house.
6 C __ mm __ n __ ty s __ rv __ c __ isn't a good punishment for a crime like fr ___ d.
7 Last year he was __ rr __ st __ d for sh __ pl __ ft __ ng.
8 The police are __ nv __ st __ g __ t __ ng the th __ ft of a famous painting.
9 In the film, he br ___ ks into a museum and sh ___ ts a security guard.

GRAMMAR present/past passive

2 Match sentence beginnings 1–8 with endings a)–h).

1 Over 4,000 foxes are
2 Our academic courses are
3 This type of clothing is
4 Until recently, charity workers weren't
5 The buildings were
6 Animal fat isn't
7 The thief was
8 That window wasn't

a) used in our food.
b) made in our factory in Milan.
c) paid much money for their work.
d) killed every year for their fur.
e) taken to prison.
f) broken by my boys.
g) designed by French architects.
h) recognised by colleges all over the world.

3 Underline the correct alternative.

My favourite crime programme is CSI, an American series. Usually it has the same structure. Firstly, someone [1]**kills/is be killed/is killed** mysteriously. After this, the CSI officers [2]**are called/call/are call** to solve the mystery. They collect evidence which [3]**looks at/is looked at/is look at** very carefully in the laboratory. Then the CSI officers [4]**are brought/have brought/bring** various people to their office and ask questions. More evidence [5]**has discovered/discovers/is discovered** which allows the CSI officers to find the killer.

So, why do I like it? The most interesting thing is the way the evidence [6]**is found/has found/is find**. They never [7]**are missed/miss/are miss** anything: a hair, a contact lens, even a dead insect. I also like the characters of the CSI officers. They are not perfect people, but they [8]**are done/do/were done** their job perfectly.

4 Complete the texts with the past simple active or passive form of the verbs in the box.

| tell | choose | say | catch | give |
| come | arrest | have | | |

A girl in North Carolina [1]_____ for theft. During her trial, she [2]_____ to go home and get her favourite possession. She [3]_____ back with her iPod. The judge threw it onto the floor and broke it. 'Now you know how it feels to lose your favourite possession,' he said. 'Don't do it to anybody else.'

William Brown, aged nineteen, [4]_____ stealing a TV from a house. Brown said the TV was for his little brother, who [5]_____ a broken leg and was bored in bed. The judge sentenced Brown to no TV-watching for a year. Amazingly, the victim of the crime [6]_____, 'It's OK. I have two TVs. He can borrow one while his brother gets better.'

Lucas Stepanovich drove through town playing loud music with his windows down. At his trial, he [7]_____ a choice: pay a $100 fine or listen to loud classical music for six hours. He [8]_____ the music.

5 Complete sentences 1–8 so they mean the same as the first sentences. Use the active or passive form of the verb in brackets.

1 Extra homework is given to the students every day.
   The students _____. (give)
2 His books aren't sold in the USA.
   The USA _____. (not sell)
3 The library was destroyed in an earthquake.
   An earthquake _____. (destroy)
4 The children didn't eat the spaghetti.
   The spaghetti _____. (not/eat)
5 Hundreds of products use plastic.
   Plastic _____. (use/in)
6 The thief was caught by the police.
   The police _____. (catch)
7 No one told us about the exam.
   We _____. (not/tell)
8 You don't find tigers in Africa.
   Tigers _____. (not/find)

LISTENING

6A ▶ 10.3 Read the text and look at the pictures. What issues do you think each person will talk about? Listen and check.

We asked people from different generations three questions:

1 What annoys you about modern life?

2 How can we stop it?

3 What punishments do you propose?

We asked a 16-year-old, a 35-year-old and a 70-year-old. You may find their answers surprising. Or maybe not!

A

B

C

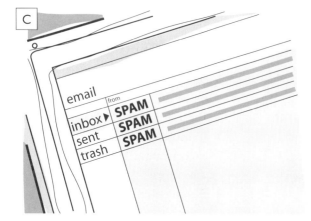

B Listen again and choose the correct option to complete the sentences.

1 Sophie _____.
   a) is a teacher
   b) works with technology
   c) is a schoolgirl

2 Sophie thinks people concentrate better _____.
   a) when they use technology
   b) without technology
   c) when they wear headphones

3 Luis doesn't like _____.
   a) newspapers and food in the tube
   b) food at work
   c) the government

4 Luis suggests a punishment: _____.
   a) cleaning the tube
   b) paying some money
   c) cleaning the streets

5 Pamela loves _____.
   a) her older friends
   b) being old
   c) technology

6 Pamela suggests a punishment: _____.
   a) working as a teacher
   b) reading emails from her
   c) reading millions of spam messages for six months

7 Read the sentences and find words that match the definitions.

1 'They spend their whole life wearing headphones. I think it's really rude.'
   not polite: _____

2 'In my school they banned personal technology during lessons.'
   formally said that people must not do something:
   _____

3 'For me, the worst thing is litter on the street.'
   unwanted paper, bottles, etc. that people leave in a public place: _____

4 'People just leave their newspapers lying around.'
   when something is left somewhere, in the wrong place:
   _____

5 'All this paper is a real mess.'
   untidy, with everything in the wrong place: _____

6 'The government has tried to introduce fines, but it hasn't worked.'
   money you have to pay as a punishment: _____

7 'Spam is so annoying.'
   makes you feel angry: _____

VOCABULARY problems

1 Use the clues to complete the crossword.

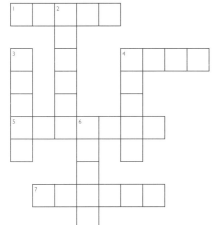

Across

1 You have to wait for something because it is late.

4 Unwanted email messages that advertise something.

5 Help that is given to you in a restaurant or shop.

7 Not working properly, e.g. equipment.

Down

2 Paper, cans, bottles, etc. that people do not want and are left in public places.

3 When a computer suddenly stops working.

4 When you can't move, e.g. in traffic or in a very small place.

6 Something that destroys information in a computer.

FUNCTION complaining

2 Circle the correct option in 1–6 below to complete the conversation.

A: Hello. Can I help at all?

B: Yes, there's a ¹_____ the television in my room.

A: What exactly is the problem?

B: It ²_____.

A: OK. I'll ³_____ it right away.

B: Thanks.

A: Is there anything else I can help you with?

B: Yes. I ordered room service this morning, but I had to wait ⁴_____ an hour.

A: I'm really ⁵_____ that, sir. Was there anything else?

B: Yes. My room was very noisy last night.

A: I'm afraid there's nothing we can ⁶_____ that, sir. There's a disco downstairs.

B: Every night?

A: Oh no, sir. On Mondays there's a rock concert.

B: Great.

1 a) problem with   b) problem for   c) big problem

2 a) isn't work   b) not work   c) doesn't work

3 a) check into   b) look into   c) look up

4 a) at over   b) for above   c) for over

5 a) sorry for   b) sorry about   c) very sorry

6 a) make about   b) do for   c) do about

3A Make sentences about the pictures using the prompts.

1 there / problem / printer

_____

2 microphone / not work

_____

3 been / over / two hours

_____

B Match complaints 1–3 above with responses a)–c).

a) I'm really sorry about that. I was stuck in a traffic jam. _____

b) I'll look into it right away. For now, you can use the photocopier on the second floor. _____

c) I'm sorry, but there's nothing we can do at the moment. We don't have any electricity. _____

LEARN TO sound firm but polite

4A Complete the sentences with a word that matches the stress pattern.

1 Sorry, but there's a _problem_ with my room. Oo

2 _____ me. I've been here over an hour. oO

3 _____ I speak to the manager? I'm not happy with the service. O

4 Could you _____ me? There's something wrong with this computer. O

5 I'm _____ I have a problem. The air conditioner in my room doesn't work. oO

6 I have to make a _____. The waitress was rude to me. oO

B ▶10.4 Listen and check. Then listen and repeat. Focus on the stressed part of each sentence.

VOCABULARY communication

1 Complete the sentences with the words in the box.

> email   webpage   internet   mobile   text   blog
> chat   send

1 Do you mind if I use your _____ phone?
2 I've just started a new _____ where I write about politics, and lots of people are reading it.
3 Could you _____ me a copy of the reservation by fax?
4 I'm just going to check my _____ for new messages.
5 Why don't you send her a _____ message?
6 We don't see each other often but we _____ a lot online.
7 Have you updated the _____ with our new photos?
8 Have you got Skype? We could talk by _____ phone.

GRAMMAR present perfect

2 Put the words in the correct order to complete the conversations.

Conversation 1
A: Are you ready for your holiday?
B: packing / I / finished / yet / haven't

_____

Conversation 2
A: Don't forget to call Amy.
B: already / to / I've / her / spoken

_____

Conversation 3
A: Hi. You look well!
B: just / from / we've / holiday / back / yes, / got

_____

Conversation 4
A: Is that the new Indiana Jones DVD?
B: haven't / yet / it / watched / yes, / I / but

_____

Conversation 5
A: my / results / just / exam / got / I've

_____

B: Tell me! How did you do?

Conversation 6
A: You need to buy a present for Josh.
B: money / but / already / all / I've / spent / my

_____

3 Complete the sentences. Use *just* and the present perfect form of the verb in brackets.

1 I'm still tired. I _____. (wake up)
2 Well done. You _____ all your work for today. (finish)
3 I don't want any lunch, thanks. I _____. (eat)
4 I don't believe it. Sam _____ his phone again. (lose)
5 That's brilliant! Helen _____ her driving test. (pass)
6 I'm really sorry. I _____ the bad news. (hear)
7 Hold on a minute, I'll check. Sheila _____ me a message. (send)
8 Let's go for a walk. It _____ raining. (stop)
9 Hurry up! The taxi _____. (arrive)
10 You're a bit late. They _____ the meeting. (start)

4A Use the prompts to complete the conversations.

Conversation 1
A: *Have you finished the book yet?* (you / finish / book / yet)
B: Yes, I've already started the next one.

Conversation 2
A: _____? (you / cook / dinner / yet)
B: No, _____. (I / only / just / get home)

Conversation 3
A: _____? (you / ask / wife / yet)
B: No, I'm going to speak to her later.

Conversation 4
A: _____? (you / decided / where / we going / yet)
B: Yes, _____. (we / just / book table / Mario's)

Conversation 5
A: Do you want to come and play football?
B: No, _____. (I / already / play / twice / this week)

Conversation 6
A: _____? (you / see / Miranda)
B: Yes, _____. (she / just / leave)

B ▶ 11.1 Listen and check.

READING

5 Read the article and choose the best title, a), b) or c).

a) The oldest blogger in the world hated the internet

b) Spain's blogging granny was a huge success

c) Spanish granny used pen and paper

'No one listens to old people,' said Maria Amelia Lopez on her blog. But she was wrong. A lot of people listened to her. When she died, aged ninety-seven, Lopez was thought to be the world's oldest blogger and she was certainly one of the most successful. Her first post was made on her ninety-fifth birthday. It read: 'Today it's my birthday and my grandson, who is very stingy, gave me a blog.'

A later post reads: 'Since that day I've had 1,570,784 visits from bloggers from five continents who have cheered up my old age.' From cleaning ladies in Brazil to the Spanish president, people have enjoyed reading what Lopez had to say. She was funny and friendly and she had some strong opinions. 'Old people need to wake up a bit,' she said. 'You have to live life. Don't take pills and fall asleep in the armchair.'

At first, Lopez didn't know anything about computers. 'I thought a blog was a kind of paper notebook,' she said. But her grandson, Daniel, who she lived with, set up a blog for her as a birthday present. At the time he had no idea how it would change their lives. Lopez received hundreds of emails, many in languages she didn't understand. Although she had helpers, including Daniel, and friends she met on the internet, she couldn't reply to everyone.

When she was on her own, Lopez loved reading the online newspapers and chatting on the internet. She said it helped her to keep in touch with the younger generation. Teenagers wrote to Lopez to tell her about their lives, and ask her for advice. She thought that everybody should use the internet. For Lopez, it was one of the best experiences of her life.

6 Read the text again. Are the statements true (T) or false (F)?

1 People from all around the world have read Maria Lopez's blog. ____

2 Lopez knew a lot about computers before she started writing the blog. ____

3 Lopez's grandson, Daniel, started the blog for his grandmother as a birthday present. ____

4 He knew that it (the internet) would change Lopez's life. ____

5 Lopez always replied to the emails she received. ____

6 The internet put Lopez in touch with younger people. ____

7 Find words or expressions in the text to match definitions 1–6.

1 a message on a website/blog (paragraph 1): _____

2 not generous; doesn't want to spend money (paragraph 1): _____

3 someone who reads/writes a blog (paragraph 2): _____

4 ideas you believe in strongly (paragraph 2): _____ _____ (2 words)

5 a comfortable chair (paragraph 2): _____

6 people aged between thirteen and twenty years old (paragraph 4): _____ _____ _____

WRITING pronouns

8 Replace words in the second sentence with the pronouns in the box.

~~there~~ it here us her them

1 We went to the beach. We had a lovely time / *there* ~~on the beach~~.

2 I visited my grandmother. I took my grandmother out to lunch.

3 I saw some friends. I hadn't seen my friends for a long time.

4 He's just started a new job. He's enjoying the new job.

5 The waiter smiled at Mark and me. Then he gave Mark and me the bill.

6 This place is so beautiful. I'd like to stay in this place for ever.

VOCABULARY feelings

1 How would you feel in these situations? Match situations 1–8 with the words in the box below.

> uncomfortable bored nervous lonely confused worried
> amazed excited

1 It's your birthday and you're having a party. _____

2 You've just bought a new computer and you are trying to read the instructions. _____

3 You are standing on a crowded train, carrying heavy bags, and you are too hot. _____

4 You have been asked to give a talk to 300 people. _____

5 You have decided to spend a year in another country, but you haven't met any friends yet. _____

6 You have got a bad cough and you have had it for more than six months. _____

7 By chance at the airport you see a friend who you haven't seen for ten years. _____

8 You are waiting in an airport and your plane has been delayed for four hours. _____

2 ▶ 11.2 Listen to people talking about their feelings. Match the feelings 1–6 with what they say about them a)–f).

1	bored	a) anything to do with numbers
2	lonely	b) prefers to be busy
3	confused	c) the beauty of nature
4	amazed	d) problems of the world
5	nervous	e) call a friend/sister
6	worried	f) organise a party/dinner

GRAMMAR first conditional + *when*

3 Match sentence beginnings 1–8 with endings a)–h).

1 We'll go for a walk
2 If she passes her exams,
3 We'll be there to meet you at the airport
4 I'm sure he'll make lots of new friends
5 If you like the music,
6 If you're very busy now,
7 They'll hear us coming in
8 If you plan your talk carefully,

a) I'll get you a CD.
b) if we make too much noise.
c) when the plane arrives.
d) if the weather gets better.
e) you'll be fine.
f) she'll go to university.
g) I'll come back later.
h) when he starts his course.

4 Complete the sentences with the correct form of the verbs in brackets.

1 If I _____ (be) late again, my girlfriend _____ (be) furious!

2 I _____ (call) you if there _____ (be) a problem.

3 When I _____ (see) Mary, I _____ (tell) her you were here.

4 If the taxi _____ (not come) soon, we _____ (be) late.

5 If I _____ (get) another job, I _____ (earn) a bit more money.

6 I _____ (buy) you some lunch if you _____ (be) hungry.

7 They _____ (change) their minds when they _____ (see) the hotel.

8 What _____ you _____ (do) if you _____ (lose) your job?

5 Complete the conversation. Use the correct form of the verbs in the box below.

stay wait not know have spend find go (x2) be look (x2) get

A: We need to book our summer holiday. If we ¹_____ any longer, everything ²_____ fully booked.

B: You're right. But we still haven't decided where to go.

A: How about Spain?

B: If we ³_____ to Spain, we should ⁴_____ good weather. But we always go to Spain.

A: Paris?

B: We could try, but if we ⁵_____ in Paris, we ⁶_____ lots of money. Paris is really expensive.

A: OK. How about Romania or Bulgaria?

B: We could try that. But if we ⁷_____ there, we ⁸_____ the language.

A: That doesn't matter.

B: I know, and if we ⁹_____ on the internet, we might ¹⁰_____ some cheap deals.

A: That's a good idea. If you ¹¹_____ time later, ¹²_____ you _____?

B: OK. But I'm not going to Paris. I don't have enough money!

6 Look at the picture and write sentences using the prompts.

1 when the man / cross / bridge / he / give / his girlfriend / flowers
   When the man crosses the bridge, he will give his girlfriend the flowers.

2 if / elephant / walk on bridge / the bridge / break
   _____

3 if / bridge / break / the elephant / fall
   _____

4 if / elephant / fall / the crocodiles / eat it
   _____

5 if / man / fall / girlfriend / scream
   _____

6 if / girlfriend / scream / snake / wake up
   _____

7 if / snake / wake up / bite / girlfriend
   _____

8 if / man / not / cross / bridge / can keep / flowers
   _____

9 if / he / keep / flowers / it / be a lot easier
   _____

7 ▶ 11.3 Listen to two people answering the question. Circle the correct answers (Yes / No) to questions 1–4.

ARE NEW COMPUTER GAMES CHANGING THE WAY WE LIVE?

	Robert	Miriam
1 Does he/she think computer games are changing the way we live?	Yes / No	Yes / No
2 Does he/she use a computer for work?	Yes / No	Yes / No
3 Does he/she enjoy computer games?	Yes / No	Yes / No
4 Does he/she think people will change how they spend their free time?	Yes / No	Yes / No

8A Complete Robert's and Miriam's statements.

Robert

1 'I think they have already _____ the way we live.'

2 'Some people already spend more _____ in virtual worlds, like Second Life, than they do in the real world.'

3 'I have meetings with my _____ in Second Life.'

4 'It's more fun and exciting than the real world where you have to worry about _____.'

Miriam

5 'There are lots of games I don't like, like the _____ games.'

6 'I don't spend all my time on the _____.'

7 'And I think a lot of people are like _____.'

8 'In our free time we _____ to do other things.'

B Listen again and check.

VOCABULARY internet terms

1 Complete the words in the sentences.

1 I write regularly on my bl__g. I talk about all kinds of things, like things I've read in the news, or funny articles. I enjoy it.

2 I use Google a lot, but I use other s___rch __ng__n__s too.

3 Sometimes I read the discussions on the m__ss__g__ b___rds. It's interesting to see what other people think about things.

4 I don't use any of the s__c___l n__tw___k__ng s__t__s because I just don't have time. I prefer to talk to friends on the phone, or send them an email.

5 I look at tr__v__l w__bs__t__s when I am planning a holiday. It's useful to get ideas of where you could go.

6 I read a few different __nl__n__ n__ws sites because I like reading news from other countries.

7 I get all my music from the m__s__c d__wnl___d sites.

8 When I've got a few minutes to spare, I look at the v__d___ sh__r__ng sites and watch funny clips.

FUNCTION giving opinions

2 Complete the conversations with the words in the box.

my   true   don't   definitely   that's   sure   totally

1 A: It's always better to do your shopping online.

B: I _____ think that's true. It's not always cheaper.

2 A: People who live in rich countries should give money to people in poorer countries.

B: In _____ opinion, that's not the best way to solve the problem.

3 A: This bar is much nicer than the one we came to last time.

B: _____. I really like it here.

4 A: If you want people to work harder, you need to pay them more money.

B: _____ right.

5 A: I think our product is the best on the market.

B: I'm not _____ about that.

6 A: You need to control how many people move into the country.

B: I _____ disagree. I think people should be allowed to live where they want.

7 A: Not everyone has a mobile phone even nowadays.

B: That's _____, although most people do.

LEARN TO disagree politely

3 Put the words in the correct order to make polite responses.

1 don't / I / sorry / think / right / I'm / but / that's

_____

2 disagree / totally / I'm / I / afraid

_____

3 not / about / I'm / sure / that / really

_____

4 sorry / don't / so / I'm / think / I / but

_____

4A Read the conversation. Change the responses in brackets to make them more polite.

Manager: The project needs to be finished this week.

Worker: ¹_____. (That's not possible.)

Manager: Why not? Everything's possible.

Worker: ²_____. (I don't think it is.) We're working hard, but we need another two weeks to finish the job.

Manager: Two weeks? Can you try to finish by the end of next week?

Worker: ³_____ (No.) There's still a lot of work to do.

Manager: That's true. But you can get some more staff, so we can finish sooner. ⁴_____. (I don't see what the problem is.)

Worker: ⁵_____. (I disagree.) The problem is that we don't have more staff. We can't find people to start work tomorrow ...

B ▶ 11.4 Listen to the conversation and check your answers.

C ▶ 11.5 Listen and repeat the phrases using polite intonation.

VOCABULARY film

1 Match the types of film in the box with descriptions 1–10.

> ~~historical drama~~   action film   comedy   western
> science fiction film   fantasy film   horror film   thriller
> musical   documentary

1 it tells a story from many years ago _historical drama_

2 it has lots of songs _____

3 it is funny _____

4 it shows something true or real and doesn't usually have actors _____

5 it is frightening _____

6 it has lots of fights, guns and explosions _____

7 it might show people from another planet or futuristic technology _____

8 it has imaginative but impossible situations _____

9 it is exciting because you don't know what will happen at the end _____

10 it usually has cowboys _____

GRAMMAR reported speech

2 Tick the correct sentences. Put a cross next to the sentences which contain mistakes.

1 a) Sandra told us she would be here at 6.00. ✓
   b) Sandra said us she would be here at 6.00. ✗

2 a) He said me he wanted to be a lawyer.
   b) He told me he wanted to be a lawyer.

3 a) I bought orange juice because you said you didn't like apple juice.
   b) I bought orange juice because you told you didn't like apple juice.

4 a) The doctor said them he couldn't cure the illness.
   b) The doctor told them he couldn't cure the illness.

5 a) Mary told to us she was writing the great American novel.
   b) Mary said she was writing the great American novel.

6 a) Luca and Giselle said us their plane would arrive at 9.30.
   b) Luca and Giselle told us their plane would arrive at 9.30.

3 Match sentence beginnings 1–10 with endings a)–j).

1 John was cooking steak, so I told him

2 Dave asked if we liked the theatre, but I told him

3 I called Reuben on his mobile, but he said

4 Maisie invited me to dinner, so I said

5 We invited him to work with us, but he said

6 I asked her if she felt OK and she told me

7 They asked if it was a boy or a girl, so I said

8 I needed help with my algebra homework, but Dad said

9 Jim asked about her tennis, but she told him

10 Our neighbour wanted a map of London, but I told her

a) we wouldn't know until June.

b) he couldn't do maths.

c) we preferred the cinema.

d) she wasn't playing any more.

e) he was working for another company.

f) we didn't have one.

g) I'd see if I was free tonight.

h) I didn't eat meat.

i) she always felt tired in the afternoon.

j) he couldn't hear me.

4 Read Bill's news and report what he says.

1 I'm an actor.
   He said he _____was an actor_____.

2 I'm starring in a TV series.
   He told me _____.

3 I'll appear in a film next year.
   He said _____.

4 The film is called *Samba Nights*.
   He told me _____.

5 I can work with any Hollywood directors I choose.
   He said _____.

6 I'm living in Beverly Hills.
   He told me _____.

7 I'm getting married to Sonia Jeffers next month.
   He said _____.

8 She is a famous actor too.
   He told _____.

9 I'll text you next week.
   He said _____.

10 I can take you to some great parties.
   He told me _____.

LISTENING

5A ▶ 12.1 Read the dictionary definition and the notes about a radio programme. Listen and complete the notes.

> **contract:** (n) formal document that explains the details of a deal

STRANGE REQUESTS IN STARS' CONTRACTS

In the old days, big studios controlled their ¹_actors_.

In his contract, Johnny Weissmuller had to weigh ²_____ pounds (about 82 kilograms) or less.

Buster Keaton could not ³_____ during his films.

These days, famous ⁴_____ have all the power.

Woody Allen's ⁵_____ went on a private tour of Disneyland. It was in his contract.

Some musicians, especially rock stars, ask for very strange things in their ⁶_____.

B Listen again and answer the questions.

1 What was Johnny Weissmuller's problem?

_____

2 How much was the bill for these in one James Bond film?

_____

3 What colour was everything in Jennifer Lopez's room?

_____

4 What type of food did this group ask for?

_____

C Match the words in bold in sentences 1–5 with definitions a)–e).

1 In the old days, big **studios** controlled their actors.
2 In his next **role**, the contract said he had to be 190 pounds or less.
3 Buster Keaton's face became so important that the studio said he could not smile **on screen**.
4 They are the **stars** and their contracts show it.
5 In her contract, Jennifer Lopez asked for a white **changing room** with white curtains.

a)
> n, [C] a character in a play or film

b)
> n, [C] a famous actor, singer, sports player, etc.

c)
> n, [C] a room where a performer (actor, singer, sportsperson) goes to change his/her clothes

d)
> n, [C] a film company, or the place where films are made

e)
> prep + n during a film or a television programme

D Complete the actor's blog using words and phrases from Exercise C. Change the form if necessary.

ActingUp.com
Actor Jack Jones's blogspot

Just found out I'm sharing a ¹_____ with Emily Sharp! She's my hero! I've seen her ²_____ lots of times and she's always brilliant. She's going to be a big ³_____. She has the biggest ⁴_____ in the film – she plays a reporter who discovers a city under the Earth. It's a fantastic story based on a great book, and I'm really happy that the ⁵_____ decided to film it. I have to go now!

posted by: Jack 12.35p.m.

<u>16 comments</u>

VOCABULARY suffixes

1 Complete the words with a suitable suffix.

1 The guide contains lots of use*ful* information.
2 He's quite famous now. He's been very success_____ in his career.
3 We've been married for forty years! We're having a celebrat_____.
4 You spent a week in the jungle? How adventur_____ of you!
5 I never believe what politic_____ say. They just want you to vote for them.
6 We've asked a photograph_____ to take the photographs.
7 It's been a wonder_____ holiday. Thank you so much.
8 I never ride motorbikes. They're too danger_____.
9 Thank you so much. You've been very help_____.

2A Put the words in the correct place in the table, according to the stress pattern.

adventurous   politician   wonderful   musician
celebrity   scientist   invention

ooOo	oOoo	oOo	Ooo
celebration	photographer	successful	dangerous
1_____	2_____	4_____	6_____
	3_____	5_____	7_____

B ▶ 12.2 **Listen and check. Repeat the words.**

GRAMMAR second conditional

3 Put the verbs in brackets into the correct tense to make conditional sentences.

1 If he _____ (not / have) a lot of money, she _____ (not / be) interested in him.
2 If I _____ (not / have) an exam tomorrow, I _____ (love) to come out with you.
3 We _____ (be) so much happier if we _____ (not / argue) all the time.
4 I'm sure she _____ (ask) you if she _____ (need) some help.
5 If it _____ (not / rain) so much, we _____ (go out) more often.
6 You _____ (not / be) so tired if you _____ (go) to bed earlier.
7 If I _____ (have) my car here, I _____ (offer) to drive you home.
8 If he _____ (able to) find a job there, he _____ (move) to Spain.

4 Make sentences with the prompts.

1 If I / be / famous / people / recognise me / on the street
   _____
2 If she / have / more money / she buy / car
   _____
3 What / you do / if / you / lose / your job?
   _____
4 If I / lose / my job / I / have to / look for another one
   _____
5 I / travel / to China / if / able to / speak Mandarin
   _____
6 If I / have more time / I do more sport
   _____
7 If I / not have a television / I read more books
   _____
8 If you / be / famous / how / your life / change?
   _____

5 Rewrite the sentences using second conditional forms.

1 I'm very tired, so I'm not going out later.
   If I wasn't so tired, I would go out later.
2 The restaurant is very expensive, so we don't eat there.
   _____
3 You don't water the garden, so it doesn't look very good.
   _____
4 I don't have Jodie's number, so I can't call her.
   _____
5 We don't have enough money, so we can't buy our own house.
   _____
6 I don't have any food in the house, or I would invite you in for lunch.
   _____
7 I don't practise every day, so I'm not very good at the guitar.
   _____
8 I spend so much time answering my email that I don't finish my other work.
   _____
9 The flights are expensive so we don't visit very often.
   _____
10 I'm very late, so I'm walking quickly.
   _____

READING

6 Read the text and complete the summary.

LONELYGIRL15 – NOT LONELY ANYMORE

1 Lonelygirl15 was known to her fans as Bree, a sixteen-year-old home-schooled American teenager. Bree lived at home with her strict parents where she recorded her private thoughts into a digital video camera and put them on the web using the name Lonelygirl15. Like many people using a videoblog, Bree seemed shy and nervous when talking about her feelings on camera. Unlike many other people, Bree attracted millions of fans and quickly became one of YouTube's most popular stars. People regularly logged on to watch Bree talk about her own love of the internet, her fights with her father, and her first kiss with her boyfriend, Daniel.

2 What happened next shocked YouTube fans around the world. A journalist discovered that the videos were fakes. Bree was not really Bree at all. She was Jessica Rose, a nineteen-year-old New Zealand-born actress living in Los Angeles. And the shows were all written by three friends who wanted to experiment with a new type of storytelling. Instead of making a traditional film, they wanted to tell the story though two- or three-minute videoblogs, to attract an audience of viewers, who would then add their comments to help decide the next part of the story. Their idea was a great success.

3 But the news only increased Jessica's fame. 'I never really thought so many people would care about my life,' Rose said. 'It's been insane. I've had so much attention given to me that I didn't expect.' When asked about Bree's character, Rose said, 'She's fun. She's just someone you would love to meet and be friends with.' But one thing is certain – she's not lonely any longer.

Lonelygirl15 was a ¹*videoblog* where an American teenager talked about her private ²_____ on a web camera. It became a success on ³_____ and millions of ⁴_____ watched it. Actually, the blog was a ⁵_____ and the character 'lonelygirl' was really an ⁶_____. She enjoyed her fame though and received a lot of attention. She thinks that Lonelygirl15 was a success because the character is a person that everyone would like to have as a ⁷_____.

7 Read the text again. Are the statements true (T) or false (F)?

1 On the blog, Bree talked about her feelings. ____
2 Bree seemed very confident when she talked on camera. ____
3 Bree talked about problems she had with her parents. ____
4 The show took a long time to become successful. ____
5 A journalist discovered that Bree was really an actress. ____
6 The people who wrote the show were friends. ____
7 They wanted to write a traditional film. ____
8 After the news, people were not interested in Jessica anymore. ____

8 Look at the words in bold. Underline the correct alternative to complete definitions 1–5 below.

1 **Strict** parents are parents who *let/don't let* you do what you want.
2 **Private thoughts** are ideas you *tell everyone about/keep to yourself*.
3 If you are **shocked**, you feel *surprised/happy*.
4 Something which is **fake** is *real/not real*.
5 If an idea is **insane**, it is *crazy/bad*.

WRITING paragraphs

9A Put the sentences in the correct order to form three paragraphs.

Introduction/Early life
___b___ , _____,
_____, _____

Career
_____, _____, _____,
_____, _____

Personal life
_____, _____, _____

a) During the 70s and 80s, Clint starred in many successful films, but it wasn't until 1990 that he won an Oscar for Director and a nomination for best actor, for his role in *Unforgiven* (1992).

b) Clint Eastwood is perhaps one of the most famous international film stars of the 20th century.

c) Although he started, he never finished his college degree in business studies.

d) He has been married twice, and also had a long-term relationship with his co-star Sondra Locke.

e) All three films were hits, particularly the third, and Eastwood became an instant international star.

f) Eastwood has seven children, from five different women.

g) Instead, he found work as an actor in B-movies and later in a well-known television programme.

h) He lives in Carmel and has been married to Dina Eastwood since 1976.

i) Born in 1930, in San Francisco, Clint Eastwood was the son of a steel worker.

j) After this success, he was given excellent roles in films like *Where Eagles Dare*, in which he starred with Richard Burton.

k) Around this time, he also started to direct films, as well as act in them.

l) In the 1960s, Clint was given important roles in western films *A Fistful of Dollars* (1964), *For a Few Dollars More* (1965) and later *The Good, the Bad and the Ugly* (1966).

B Write your own biography (or invent one) using the headings in Exercise 9A (100–150 words).

VOCABULARY collocations

1 Underline the correct alternative.

TravelBig.com

WHAT OUR CLIENTS SAY ABOUT US

We paid a lot for our holiday with TravelBig, but it was definitely worth it. Lena, our guide, did so many things for us! On the first night, there was a concert we wanted to go to, and she ¹*took/did/got* tickets for us. On the second day, we ²*worked/rented/invited* a car and drove around the nearby towns. She ³*offered/ requested/recommended* a great place – the old ruins just outside the town – and she even ⁴*organised/ made/paid* a private tour for us! On our final night, we ⁵*helped/offered/invited* Lena to dinner and she ⁶*bought/booked/rented* a table in one of the best restaurants I have ever been to. I would definitely recommend TravelBig.

Pablo Gonzalez

FUNCTION requests and offers

2 Match sentence beginnings 1–7 with endings a)–g).

1 I'd
2 Would it be
3 Would you be able to
4 Could you recommend
5 Shall I book a
6 Do you want me
7 Would

a) get me a ticket for the concert?
b) table for four?
c) to ask for a better seat?
d) possible to invite my cousin?
e) you like me to call a taxi?
f) a good dentist?
g) like to rent a boat for six people.

3 Complete the sentences using the pairs of words in the box.

you recommend	would like	like me	be possible
want me	shall I	able to	

1 They _____ _____ a holiday in a hot country.
2 Would it _____ _____ to rent a car at the airport?
3 Would you be _____ _____ get me a ticket?
4 Could _____ _____ a good doctor?
5 _____ _____ speak to your teacher about the problem?
6 Do you _____ _____ to take that bag for you?
7 Would you _____ _____ to find a good restaurant?

LEARN TO ask for more time

4 Underline the correct alternatives to complete the conversations.

1 **A:** Would it be possible to get an appointment with Dr Jones?
  B: Can you *get/give* me a moment? I'll see if he has any time this week.

2 **A:** Do you have Paula's phone number?
  B: Hang *on/off*. I don't know where I put my mobile.

3 **A:** Is this a good time to discuss the agenda for the meeting?
  B: Just *the/a* moment. There's another caller on the line.

4 **A:** Johnny! Open the door!
  B: Hold *in/on*! I'm in the shower!

LISTENING

5A ▶ 12.3 Listen and match pictures A–C with conversations 1–3

A

B

C

B Listen again and complete the table.

	1	2	3
1 What do the customers want?			
2 Do they get what they want?			

GRAMMAR uses of *like*

1 Complete the conversations using the prompts in brackets.

1 A: What kind of music _do you like_? (like)

   B: I like all kinds of things; Indie, Hard Rock and Dance.

2 A: Is that the new John Grisham book? _____? (what)

   B: It's great. I can't put it down.

3 A: _____ eating out in restaurants? (like)

   B: Not really. I prefer eating takeaways.

4 A: I haven't met Emelie's new boyfriend yet. _____ ? (he / like)

   B: He's really nice, and he's handsome too.

5 A: Do you get on well with your sister? _____ doing the same things? (do / like)

   B: Yes, we do. We're both very sociable. We like going out to parties.

6 A: Is it cold today? _____ weather _____? (what / like)

   B: No, it's not cold at all. The sun's shining.

VOCABULARY describing a city

2 Complete the sentences with the words in the box.

| buildings | pollution | crime | safe | nightlife | polite |
| transport | traffic | | | | |

1 It's a very _____ area. There is hardly any crime at all.

2 There are a lot of factories around the city, so the _____ is quite bad.

3 I try to use public _____, so I get the bus or the train.

4 It's a bad time of day to go by car. There's so much _____.

5 There are parties most nights, and good clubs to go to. The _____ is great.

6 I love the cities in Italy. They have so many beautiful _____.

7 People in the shops are friendly and _____. They smile, and say 'Good morning'.

8 The _____ in the area is much worse nowadays. It's dangerous to walk alone at night.

GRAMMAR present/past passive

3 Underline the correct alternatives.

Seven thousand five hundred dollars [1]finds/was found in a shoe box by a lady who [2]works/is worked in a charity shop in the USA. Teodora Petrova, who recently [3]arrived/was arrived from Bulgaria, [4]found/was found the money on her first day at work at the shop. The money [5]was hidden/hid inside a pair of shoes which had been left at the shop. When Teodora made the discovery, she immediately [6]gave/was given the money to her manager. The charity bosses [7]told/were told what happened. They [8]asked/were asked what they plan to do, and they have said that they are looking for the person who [9]gave/was given the shoes to the shop, as they probably [10]left/was left the money inside by accident. If the owner of the money [11]is not found/doesn't find, the money will be kept by the charity.

VOCABULARY crime and punishment

4 Complete the words in the sentences.

1 Statistics show that short prison sentences are not as effective as community s__rv__c__ in stopping crimes.

2 The police took my car away and I had to pay a f__n__.

3 Twenty-five percent of the people who get caught sh__pl__ft__ng are aged between thirteen and seventeen. They do it because they're bored.

4 People who bank and shop online can easily become victims of fr____d.

5 An old man stopped the th____f as he tried to run away from the bank.

6 He always drives too fast, so he was stopped for sp____d__ng.

7 The sides of the trains are always covered in gr__ff__t__.

8 I'm not drinking alcohol tonight. I don't want to be caught drink dr__v__ng.

GRAMMAR present perfect

5 Complete the conversations using the prompts.

1 A: Have you seen my files anywhere?

   B: Yes, I _'ve just put_ them on your desk. (just / put)

2 A: Have you put the rubbish out yet?

   B: Yes, I _____ it. (just / do)

3 A: Have you asked Stefan if we can stay?

   B: No, I _____ him _____. (not / ask / yet)

4 A: Do we need to pay the electrician?

   B: No, I _____ him. (already / pay)

5 A: Have you finished your work yet?

   B: No, I _____ only _____. (just / start)

6 A: Has the post arrived yet?

   B: Yes, the postman _____ it. (just / bring)

7 A: Have you had lunch already? It's only 12 o'clock.

   B: Yes, I _____ it. (just / finish)

VOCABULARY problems; communication

6 Put the underlined letters in the correct order to complete the sentences.

1 I can't stand it! That's the third time my computer has desrach _____ this morning.

2 The printer doesn't work. I think it's yaflut _____.

3 I don't know where he is. I'll send him a xett _____.

4 Have you seen Anakin's bapegwe _____? He has put some beautiful photos there.

5 I didn't know anything about it, so I looked on one of the shecra _____ engines.

6 My computer's not working. I think it's got a sruvi _____.

7 I sent you an limae _____. Didn't you get it?

8 I don't buy newspapers anymore. I read the niolen _____ news.

GRAMMAR first and second conditionals

7 Underline the correct alternative to complete the sentences.

1 If I were you, I *will/would* talk to him about the problem.
2 If the traffic is bad, I *will/would* be late.
3 If I *know/knew* the answer, I would tell you.
4 You *will/would* miss the train if you don't hurry up.
5 If I *am/was* the president, I would change the law.
6 If he works hard, he *will/would* get a pay rise.
7 I'm sure they'll have children if they *get/got* married.
8 If we *leave/left* the country, my mother wouldn't be very happy.

VOCABULARY feelings

8 Circle the best option to complete the sentences, a) or b).

1 There's nothing to do here except lie on the beach. I'm really _____.
   a) confused   b) bored.
2 She spends a lot of time on her own. I think she's very _____.
   a) excited   b) lonely
3 I didn't know anyone at the party, so I felt a little _____.
   a) uncomfortable   b) amazed
4 I've got an interview for a new job tomorrow and I'm really _____.
   a) nervous   b) bored
5 Everybody is telling me to do different things. I'm really _____.
   a) lonely   b) confused.
6 Paolo's not answering his phone. I'm _____ that something has happened to him.
   a) confused   b) worried

VOCABULARY suffixes

9 Add suffixes to the word stems in the box to complete the sentences.

| ~~danger~~ politic photograph wonder help success |

1 Why do you drive so fast? It's _dangerous_.
2 He's been a very _____ actor. Now, he's a millionaire.
3 I studied politics at university, but I decided not to become a _____.
4 We told the receptionist about the problem, and she was really _____.
5 It was a _____ evening. I enjoyed it very much.
6 I've always enjoyed taking photos. I've been a professional _____ for about ten years now.

GRAMMAR reported speech

10 Find and correct the mistakes. There is a mistake in each sentence.

1 Suzie told to me that they wanted to move house.
2 We said her that we wouldn't be long.
3 I called a taxi but they told they were busy.
4 They asked to move to a different table but the waitress said them that it wasn't possible.
5 My sister worked at the school, but last week they told she to look for another job.
6 'It was a terrible journey,' the old man told. 'I thought it would never end.'

VOCABULARY film

11 Complete the sentences with the correct type of film.

1 *The Good, The Bad and the Ugly* is my favourite _western_. I enjoy cowboy films.
2 It's a brilliant _____ film. I laughed all the way through.
3 I can't watch _____ films. I'm too scared.
4 It's an _____ film, so there are a lot of car chases.
5 *Atonement* is a _____ drama about WWII.
6 I don't like _____ films about aliens coming from space.

FUNCTION revision

12A Complete conversations 1–3 with the phrases in the boxes.

| there's a problem   I'm sorry about that   could you help |

1 A: Excuse me, _____ me?
   B: Yes, of course. What can I do?
   A: _____ with my key. It doesn't open the door.
   B: _____. I'll get you another one.

| there's nothing we can do   I'm afraid I have
excuse me, could I speak to |

2 A: _____ the manager?
   B: Yes. I'll just get him for you.
   A: _____ a complaint.
   C: What seems to be the problem?
   A: We still haven't had our main course.
   C: I'm sorry, but _____ at the moment. We're very busy.

| certainly   would you like me to   no problem
could you recommend |

3 A: _____ a good place to go shopping?
   B: _____. There's a new shopping centre not far from here. _____ order you a taxi?
   A: That would be great. Thank you.
   B: _____.

B ▶ RC4.1 Listen and check.

TEST

Circle the correct option to complete the sentences.

1 I haven't met the boss yet. What _____ like?
   a) do she   b) is she   c) are they

2 So, you're enjoying life in Argentina. What _____ about it?
   a) are you like   b) does you like   c) do you like

3 There's nothing we can do. The toys _____ here.
   a) are not made   b) don't made   c) do not make

4 Everyone in the hotel _____ by police. They still don't know who did it.
   a) interviewed   b) was interviewed
   c) were interviewed

5 People _____ to prison when they commit a crime.
   a) send   b) were sent   c) are sent

6 The internet connection doesn't _____.
   a) fix   b) on   c) work

7 We'll look into it _____ away.
   a) right   b) for   c) go

8 Why is everyone talking so _____?
   a) loud   b) loudly   c) noisy

9 There were terrible _____ at the airport.
   a) litter   b) delays   c) service

10 There are so many people at the party. The room is very _____.
   a) crowded   b) empty   c) safe

11 Why do you keep calling him? You've _____ called him three times this morning!
   a) just   b) yet   c) already

12 _____ the invitations yet?
   a) Do send   b) Have you sent
   c) Were they send

13 If I pass my test, _____ take you out to celebrate.
   a) I'd   b) I'll   c) I do

14 I've read the instructions twice, but I'm _____. I still don't know how it works.
   a) bored   b) confused   c) lonely

15 I'm not _____ about that.
   a) keen   b) fine   c) sure

16 In my _____, we should all pay less tax.
   a) opinion   b) thinking   c) idea

17 It's my husband's new car, so I'm very _____ when I drive it.
   a) amazed   b) confused   c) nervous

18 We're going on holiday tomorrow. I'm really _____.
   a) excited   b) lonely   c) bored

19 Listen to this. I've just _____ their new album from the website.
   a) downstairs   b) downloaded   c) downsized

20 Hi, everyone. Welcome to my weekly _____.
   a) blog   b) search engine   c) website

21 I _____ her we would be late.
   a) said   b) asked   c) told

22 The tour guide _____ we should stay here.
   a) said   b) told   c) asked

23 What would you do if she _____ her job?
   a) leave   b) leaves   c) left

24 If we had more money, we _____ go on expensive holidays.
   a) would   b) will   c) won't

25 If I _____ the lottery, I wouldn't tell anyone.
   a) win   b) will win   c) won

26 I watched a very good _____ about police in South Africa.
   a) horror film   b) western   c) documentary

27 I enjoy _____ films best. They make me laugh.
   a) comedy   b) horror   c) action

28 He's a great _____. I saw his exhibition.
   a) photography   b) photographer   c) photograph

29 You want to speak to Daniel? _____ a moment, here he is.
   a) Hold   b) Just   c) Just one

30 Can you hold _____? I'll be with you in a minute.
   a) up   b) in   c) on

TEST RESULT _____ /30

76

AUDIOSCRIPT

UNIT 1 Recording 1

1 play_ed_ stay_ed_ tri_ed_ end_ed_
2 ask_ed_ kiss_ed_ arriv_ed_ talk_ed_
3 finish_ed_ decid_ed_ pretend_ed_ want_ed_
4 studi_ed_ happen_ed_ invent_ed_ stay_ed_
5 walk_ed_ help_ed_ stopp_ed_ start_ed_

UNIT 1 Recording 2

Priscilla Beaulieu was just fourteen years old when she met Elvis Presley in Germany. He was a soldier and was ten years older than her, but they got on well and spent a lot of time together. When Elvis returned to the USA, he told Priscilla that he wanted her to come with him. Priscilla loved the idea, but her parents were not so happy. When Elvis was in America, he wrote Priscilla letters and sent her records of his favourite artists and songs. They talked on the phone two to three times a week over the next two years and fell very much in love.

In the summer of 1962, Elvis decided that phone calls and letters were not enough and he invited Priscilla to Los Angeles. Priscilla went on several holidays to the USA to stay with Elvis. Eventually, Elvis asked Priscilla's parents if she could come and live with his parents in the house next to his. When her father agreed, in 1963, Priscilla moved to Memphis to be near Elvis. She was just seventeen years old.

Four years later, in 1967, Priscilla and Elvis got married, and nine months later they had a daughter, Lisa Marie. At first they were very happy together, but as Elvis became more famous, he travelled a lot, and the problems started. Priscilla stayed at home and felt bored. She decided to start karate lessons, so she took lessons with a teacher, Mike Stone, a few times a week, and enjoyed it very much. When she argued with Elvis, Priscilla found it easy to talk to Mike about her feelings. Priscilla and Mike got to know each other well, and eventually they started to go out together. Priscilla soon left Elvis for Mike, and in 1972 Elvis and Priscilla got divorced. But they stayed good friends until Elvis died on August 16, 1977.

UNIT 1 Recording 3

1 Do you like it here?
2 Where are you going?
3 I come from Italy.
4 It's a beautiful day.
5 I'm afraid I can't remember.
6 Where did you buy it?
7 I'm sorry, but I don't understand.

UNIT 1 Recording 4

1 Did you have a nice weekend?
2 Where did you go?
3 Would you like a drink?
4 So, do you like it here?
5 It was nice to meet you.
6 Let's keep in touch.

UNIT 2 Recording 1

7 syllables: motorcycle courier
6 syllables: foreign correspondent
5 syllables: fashion designer,
          IT consultant, personal trainer
4 syllables: rescue worker
2 syllables: sales rep

UNIT 2 Recording 2

1 People who work sitting down always get paid more than people who work standing up.
2 The successful people are usually the ones who listen more than they talk.
3 Politicians never believe what they say so they are surprised when other people do.
4 Once in a while, teachers will open a door, if you're lucky, but you have to enter alone.
5 Great artists like Van Gogh rarely live to see their success.
6 Doctors are the same as lawyers. The only difference is that lawyers rob you, but doctors rob you **and** kill you occasionally.
7 Find something you love doing, and you'll never have to work a day in your life.
8 The only place where success always comes before work is in the dictionary.

UNIT 2 Recording 3

Story 1

I work on a safari as a guide. I take tourists to see the animals. Everyone thinks my job is dangerous, but I don't think so. Well, I *didn't* think so until last month. So, what happened? Well, I had a bus full of tourists. There were fifteen of them. It was a beautiful, clear evening, and about seven o'clock we saw some elephants. Everyone wanted to take photos so I told them they could get off the bus for a few minutes. So there we were – these tourists taking photos of the elephants. Then suddenly the male elephant turned. It looked at us. And I could see that it was angry. So I told everyone to stand still. 'Don't move.' Well, the elephant continued looking at us and I thought that it was going to charge, you know, to run at us. I told the tourists to walk very slowly back to the bus. Then the elephant charged at us. I jumped into the bus and started driving as fast as possible. The elephant came very close and the tourists were all shouting and screaming. But it was OK in the end. We escaped.

Story 2

I was on a safari holiday. It was a really beautiful place, very quiet. One evening, at about six o'clock, we went for a drive in the tour bus. There were twenty of us tourists. Well, we soon saw some elephants. They were drinking at a pool. So we got out of the bus to take photos. Anyway, suddenly this large male elephant started looking very angry. Then it walked towards us. The guide told us to run back to the bus as fast as possible. So we did. This was a really bad idea because the elephant followed us. Then the guide got into the bus and drove away very fast. We were really quiet and calm because we didn't want to frighten the elephant. But it wasn't a nice experience and we were happy to get back to the hotel that night.

UNIT 2 Recording 4

1 I'm very keen on cooking and I absolutely love great food.
2 I love riding my motorbike. I can't stand sitting in an office all day.
3 I'm quite keen on technology and I don't mind dealing with other people's computer problems.
4 I'm very keen on working with money and I don't like people wasting it on stupid things.

UNIT 2 Recording 5/6

Conversation 1

A: On Saturday I went to a conference about the z-phone, this amazing new technology.
B: That sounds interesting.
A: Well, everybody's talking about it.
B: So how does it work?
A: Oh, I don't know. I didn't go to the presentations. I only went for the free food.

Conversation 2

A: Today I was offered a job as a babysitter.
B: That's great!
A: Not really. They only offered me five euros an hour.
B: Oh, I see. So did you accept the job?
A: No. I'm going to look for something better.
B: Right. What did you tell them?
A: I said, 'Dad, I know the baby is my sister, but I want a better salary!'

UNIT 3 Recording 1

classical exhibition composer
performance sculptor songwriter
paintings concert

UNIT 3 Recording 2

D = David   T = Terry

D: So what do you think, Terry? I put it on this wall because of the light.

T: Um. It's … it's … well, I want to say I like it. But I don't.

D: You don't like it?

T: No, David. I don't. It's terrible.

D: What?

T: It's just black. All over. It's black on black. It looks like a painting of a black bird flying over a black building on a black night.

D: It's modern art, Terry.

T: I know, I know. But it doesn't say anything.

D: What do you mean, it doesn't say anything? It's art. It doesn't talk.

T: You know what I mean. It has no message. I don't understand it.

D: You don't have to understand it, Terry. It's art. It just exists. It's not there to be understood.

T: So why is it all black? Why not white? Or white and black? Or red, white and black?

D: Why don't you ask the artist?

T: How much did it cost?

D: I'm not telling you.

T: How much did it cost?

D: Why?

T: I want to know.

D: It was expensive.

T: What does that mean? What's expensive? Fifty dollars? Fifty thousand dollars?

D: Nearer fifty thousand.

T: Nearer fifty thousand dollars than fifty?

D: Yes. Forty-five thousand. Forty-five thousand dollars.

T: I can't believe it. You bought a black painting … you spent forty-five thousand dollars …

D: I liked it. I like it. No, I love it.

T: It's black, David. Black on black. I could paint it for you in five minutes.

D: But you didn't.

T: You didn't ask me to.

D: I didn't want you to.

T: Has Mary seen it?

D: Not yet. She's away. She'll be back on Friday.

T: Does she know you bought it?

D: No. It's a surprise.

T: Oh yes, it will be. A big surprise. Does Mary even like modern art?

D: Yes. She'll like this.

T: How do you know?

D: I know.

T: How?

D: Because I know what Mary likes and what Mary doesn't like. And she'll like this.

T: I hope so. Because if she doesn't, you're dead.

UNIT 3 Recording 3

Conversation 1

D = Danny   P = Pauline

D: You've reached Danny's voicemail. Please leave a message.

P: Hi, Danny. It's Pauline here. I'm calling about tomorrow night. Unfortunately, there are no more tickets for the concert. I called them at about two o'clock, but they were already sold out. So … I don't know what you want to do. Anyway, give me a call tonight after six. Bye.

Conversation 2

E = Elise   W = Woman

E: Hi, is Tricia there, please?

W: No, I'm afraid she isn't. Who's speaking?

E: It's Elise here.

W: Hi, Elise. No, I'm afraid Tricia is out at the moment. D'you want to leave a message?

E: Yes, can you tell her I'll be at the station at eight. She's going to meet me there.

W: Sorry, can you repeat that?

E: Yes. I'll be at the station at eight.

W: Oh, OK. At eight. I'll tell her that.

E: Thanks. Oh, and can you tell her that her mobile isn't working?

W: Yes, OK. I think she needs to recharge it.

E: Thanks. Bye.

W: Bye.

Conversation 3

A: Roundhouse Bar and Grill. How can I help you?

B: Oh hello there. I'd like to book a table for three people for Wednesday evening.

A: Oh, we don't take bookings actually.

B: Oh really?

A: Yeah, if you just show up at the door, that'll be fine.

B: OK.

A: Around eight is usually our busiest time, between eight and nine-thirty. So if you come a bit before that …

B: Great. Thanks very much for your help.

A: You're welcome.

RC1 Recording 1

Conversation 1

A: Hello. My name's Felipe. It's nice to meet you.

B: Hi, I'm Magda. Nice to meet you too.

Conversation 2

A: It's a lovely day, isn't it?

B: Yes, the weather's beautiful.

Conversation 3

A: So, where exactly do you come from?

B: Zaragoza. It's a small city in Northern Spain.

Conversation 4

A: Did you have a good weekend?

B: Yes, I had a lovely time, thank you.

Conversation 5

A: So, would you like a drink?

B: Yes, I'd love a glass of water.

Conversation 6

A: It was nice to meet you, Magda.

B: Yes, let's try to keep in touch.

UNIT 4 Recording 1

1 How much do I have to pay?
2 Can I park here?
3 We must visit her before we leave.
4 We don't have to stay in this hotel.
5 She can't wear that!
6 You mustn't tell anyone.

UNIT 4 Recording 2

I = Interviewer   P = Professor

I: Professor Morris, we're looking at learning and the different ways in which people like to learn. And one of the things we can look at is the type of learner. Is that right?

P: Yes, research has shown that there may be many different types of learner. But one way we can look at this is to divide people into two groups: holists and serialists. Now, most people will probably use both approaches, but often we find people are quite strongly one or the other.

I: Holists and serialists. So, what's the difference between the two?

P: Well, students who are serialists like to study taking one step at a time. They look at a subject or topic and work through the different parts of the topic in order.

I: And holistic learners? How are they different?

P: The holists are very different. They like to have a general understanding of the whole topic. And they find it easier to study and learn if they have an idea of the 'big picture'. They don't worry so much about the detail.

I: Oh. That's me. I think I'm more of a holist.

P: Are you? Well, you see …

UNIT 4 Recording 3

I = Interviewer   P = Professor

I: So, tell me a little bit more about the serialist. You said that they like to learn things in sequence, in order.

P: That's right. So, they start at the beginning, and when they feel they've fully understood one part, then they are ready to move onto the next part. But it's very important to them that they understand the detail.

I: OK. These are the kind of people who always read the instructions before they try a new piece of equipment or machinery.

P: That's right.

I: And what about the holistic learners?

P: OK. Well, a holist never starts learning about a topic at the beginning. They jump around and get lots of information. So, they might pick up a book about the topic and choose a chapter in the middle and start reading there.

I: That's like me. I choose the bit I'm most interested in.

P: Exactly. But a serialist learner will start at the beginning and read each chapter in order.

I: That's very interesting. What about writing? Is there a difference there too?

P: Yes, absolutely. A serialist will make a careful plan of everything they have to write and then begin to research each area. But a holist will read about a lot of different things and have lots of bits of paper with notes. Then they will try to put the different pieces together when they begin writing.

I: That's very true. There is paper everywhere. I think my tutors at university would like me to be more serialist.

P: Yes, that's probably true …

UNIT 4 Recording 4/5

Conversation 1

A: Why don't we go to the cinema tonight?

B: That's a good idea. Do you know what's on?

Conversation 2

A: I don't think you should buy that car.

B: You're right. It's too expensive.

Conversation 3

A: I think we should organise a party.

B: I'm not sure that's a good idea. We're too busy.

Conversation 4

A: Maybe you should say sorry.

B: I suppose so. I'll call Louise later.

Conversation 5

A: You shouldn't play so many computer games.

B: You're right. I need to get out more.

Conversation 6

A: I think you should study more.

B: I suppose so. I want to do well in the exam.

UNIT 5 Recording 1

1 We were open. We were opening the shop.

2 I was fine. I was finding it difficult.

3 They were right. They were writing a book.

4 It was you. It was using too much gas.

5 She was clean. She was cleaning the house.

6 Where were you? Where were you going?

UNIT 5 Recording 2

A twenty-one-year-old German tourist called Tobi Gutt wanted to visit his girlfriend in Sydney, Australia. Unfortunately, he typed the wrong destination on a travel website. He landed near Sidney, Montana, in the United States, 13,000 kilometres away. This is his story.

Tobi left Germany for a four-week holiday. He was wearing a T-shirt and shorts, perfect clothes for the Australian summer. But the plane didn't land in Australia. It landed in freezing cold Montana, in the United States.

He had to take a connecting flight, but when he looked at the plane to Sidney, he became confused. Strangely, it was very small. And then he realised his mistake. Sidney, Montana, was an oil town of about 5,000 people. It was also in the United States, not Australia.

Tobi then spent three days waiting in the airport. He had only a thin jacket in the middle of winter, and no money. A few friendly people helped him with food and drink until eventually, his parents and friends from Germany sent him some money. He bought a ticket to Australia, where finally he saw his girlfriend.

UNIT 5 Recording 3

1 A twenty-one-year-old German tourist called Tobi Gutt wanted to visit his girlfriend in Sydney, Australia. Unfortunately, he typed the wrong destination on a travel website.

2 When he looked at the plane to Sidney, he became confused. Strangely, it was very small.

3 A few friendly people helped him with food and drink until eventually, his parents and friends from Germany sent him some money.

UNIT 5 Recording 4

Conversation 1

Go along Hemingway Road. Go past The Bellow Club and take the first left. It's next to the Baldwin Bar.

Conversation 2

Go along Hemingway Road, then take the first right. You'll be on Morrison Road. Go along Morrison Road for about five minutes, past the turning for the car park. It's in front of you.

Conversation 3

Go along Hemingway Road. Keep going until you reach Carver Street. Turn right on Carver Street and it's the first building on your right.

Conversation 4

Go straight along Hemingway Road. Take the second right. You'll be on Cheever Road. Go along Cheever Road. Go past the school. It's on your right.

Conversation 5

Go straight along Hemingway Road. Keep going until you reach Nabokov Street. Turn left on Nabokov Street. Go straight on. There's a river, the Faulkner River. Cross the bridge and it's in front of you.

Conversation 6

Go along Hemingway Road. Take the first right on Morrison Road. Then take the first left. There's a hospital. It's next to the hospital.

UNIT 5 Recording 5

Conversation 1

A: Excuse me. Can you help me? I'm looking for the Science Museum.

B: Go straight on. You can't miss it.

A: OK, so it's easy! Can you show me on the map?

B: Yes, of course.

Conversation 2

A: Excuse me. I'm trying to find the internet café. Is this the right way?

B: Yes. Keep going. You'll see it in front of you.

A: Can I walk?

B: Yes, you can. It takes about ten minutes.

Conversation 3

A: Is it far to the tube?

B: No. It's about two minutes' walk.

A: OK. So I need to go left at the cinema?

B: That's right. It's easy!

UNIT 6 Recording 1

1 I've known her for ages.

2 They've travelled a lot.

3 He's never seen it before.

4 Nothing has changed.

5 I've worked in other countries.

UNIT 6 Recording 2/3

Part 1

P = Presenter   W = Woman

P: We're in Manchester, and this is table tennis for the over fifties. The people who play here play three times a week, so you don't need to tell them about how exercise makes you feel better.

W: It gives you a great feeling. You feel fabulous. Any type of exercise is good for you, especially when you're my age. It just makes you feel good.

P: Scientists have now worked out that you can live longer if you have a healthy lifestyle. They did some research. They followed 20,000 people for more than ten years, and they looked at the different lifestyles they had. The results are interesting. They showed that people who don't smoke, who do regular exercise and who eat five portions of fresh fruit and vegetables every day actually live longer. These people actually live about fourteen years longer than the people who didn't have such healthy lifestyles. They lived longer and they didn't have so many health problems. Doctors say that even making a small change to your lifestyle can make a big difference to your health. Also, don't worry if you've got bad habits now. It's never too late to start.

So, does everyone agree that it's a good idea to give up smoking, eat healthily, and do exercise in order to live longer? We asked people on the street to tell us what they think.

Part 2

W2 = Woman 2   W3 = Woman 3
M = Man   P = Presenter

W2: I don't know. I don't think it's that important. I mean, I don't eat five portions of fruit and vegetables every day. I don't like them, so I'm not going to do that.

W3: If I go out with my friends in the evening, then I'm going to smoke. Having a cigarette is social. It's part of the fun.

M: Absolutely. I think it's a great idea. Do exercise, eat well, stop smoking. And live a long and happy life. Everyone should do it.

P: The message is clear: Scientists are telling us that if we want to live a long and healthy life, we need to look at how we live. So, I'm going to have a game of table tennis.

UNIT 6   Recording 4

Conversation 1

D = Doctor   W = Woman

D: Good morning. How can I help?
W: I'm worried about my leg.
D: Your leg? What's the matter with it?
W: Well, it's very painful. It hurts when I walk.
D: I see. How long have you had the problem?
W: Since yesterday.
D: Can I have a look?
W: Yes, of course.

Conversation 2

D = Doctor   M = Man

D: Hello. What's the matter, Mr Smith?
M: I feel terrible.
D: All right. Where does it hurt?
M: Everywhere. And I can't sleep.
D: Ah. Have you got a temperature?
M: I don't know.
D: OK. Can I have a look?

M: Yes, of course.
D: That's fine. It's nothing to worry about.
M: But I feel terrible!

UNIT 6   Recording 5

Conversation 1

D = Doctor   P1 = Patient 1

D: Good afternoon. What's the matter?
P1: I've got a sore throat and a headache.
D: I see. How long have you had the problem?
P1: About two weeks.
D: Have you got a temperature?
P1: Yes. It's 38.5, so I've taken some aspirin.
D: I see. I think you've got a cold. You need plenty of rest and hot drinks.

Conversation 2

P2 = Patient 2   D = Doctor

P2: I think I've broken my arm.
D: Oh dear. Can I have a look?
P2: Yes. Here you are.
D: So, where does it hurt?
P2: Here, and here.
D: How did you do it?
P2: I fell over.
D: I think you should go to hospital for an X-ray.

RC2   Recording 1

D = Doctor   P = Patient

D: Good morning. What's the problem?
P: I have a backache all the time, and it hurts when I walk.
D: I see. How long have you had this problem?
P: About two weeks.
D: Can I have a look? Where does it hurt?
P: Here. It's very painful. Sometimes I can't sleep because of the pain.
D: OK, I'll give you some medicine for it. And you shouldn't do any heavy work for a few weeks.
P: But I'm worried about missing work. I'm a builder.
D: You need to rest for at least two weeks. I'll write a note. OK?
P: OK. Thanks, doctor.

UNIT 7   Recording 1

1 She used to be very shy.
2 I didn't use to have a car.
3 My granddad used to give me sweets.
4 I never used to study at school.
5 They used to live in America.
6 Did you use to go to the cinema?

UNIT 7   Recording 2

1 used to be … She used to be very shy.
2 didn't use to have … I didn't use to have a car.
3 used to give … My granddad used to give me sweets.

4 used to study … I never used to study at school.
5 used to live … They used to live in America.
6 Did you use to … Did you use to go to the cinema?

UNIT 7   Recording 3

I = Interviewer   S = Susan

I: So, Susan, why do people change their names?
S: There are many reasons. Some of them are quite simple. For example, when a woman gets divorced, she might want to go back to her original name.
I: Right.
S: And of course other people just don't like their names. But then there are more interesting reasons.
I: Can you give us some examples?
S: Well, the boxer Muhammad Ali was originally called Cassius Clay. When he changed his religion, he also changed his name to Muhammad Ali.
I: So, religious reasons.
S: Yes. And for famous people – especially actors and singers – they need a name that's easy to say and easy to remember. So, for example, the singer Farookh Balsara …
I: Who's that?
S: Farookh Balsara was the real name of Freddie Mercury …
I: From Queen.
S: That's right. The lead singer of Queen. And of course Freddie Mercury is easier to remember than Farookh Balsara. Or Georgios Kyriacos Panayiotou …
I: Who?
S: Georgios Kyriacos Panayiotou is the real name of the singer George Michael.
I: Ah.
S: It's the same with lots of singers, actually. Sting's real name is Gordon Sumner. The singer from U2, Bono – his real name is Robert Hewson, and so on and so on. Now another reason people want to change their name, especially if they are immigrants from another country, is to identify with the new country. So maybe you're from Germany and your real name is Wilhelm. When you go to the United States, you might change it to William. Or your name is Andreas and you change it to Andrew.
I: This probably happens a lot in the United States and England.
S: Exactly. People want to mix with others. And having a name that's easy to recognise and to pronounce helps a lot. Another reason people change their names is to separate themselves from their family or from famous parents. Angelina Jolie's father is the actor John Voight. She was originally called Angelina Jolie Voight.

I: But she dropped the name Voight.

S: That's right. And another reason for people changing their names is that there was a mistake. Oprah Winfrey's mother named her Orpah Winfrey. O-r-p-a-h. But there was a mistake on her birth certificate and everyone called her Oprah.

UNIT 7 Recording 4

Conversation 1

A: It's next to the bookshop.

B: The bookshop? The one near the cafeteria?

A: That's right.

Conversation 2

A: You can't bring your bag into the library.

B: So, do I have to leave it here?

A: That's right.

Conversation 3

A: The exam starts at 9 o'clock.

B: Did you say 9 o'clock?

A: That's right.

Conversation 4

A: I need to buy a notebook.

B: You need to buy a notebook? There's a stationery shop over there.

A: Thank you.

Conversation 5

A: Can you tell me where the study centre is?

B: It's on the left as you go out of the building.

A: Sorry, can you say that again, please?

B: It's on the left as you go out of the building.

A: Thank you.

Conversation 6

A: Where can I find Professor Adams?

B: He's in the lecture theatre.

A: Did you say 'in the lecture theatre'?

B: Yes, he's giving a presentation.

UNIT 8 Recording 1

1 I gave it up.
2 Eventually I gave in.
3 When are you going to give back that book?
4 This desk takes up too much space.
5 We took over the company.
6 I'm taking it back to the shop.

UNIT 8 Recording 2

Maggie and Joe Smith lived in the same house for fifty years. When Maggie was eighty-six years old, Joe died. The house was very big so Maggie decided to move. She sold the house to a businessman called David Jones. A few weeks later, Maggie was at the hairdresser when she heard someone say that the new owner, David Jones, had found some money in her old house. She contacted Mr Jones. He told her there was $10,000 hidden in the wall. Then he said they could share the money: $5,000 for him and $5,000 for her. She agreed. A few days later, Mr Jones visited Maggie Smith. He had a contract. The contract said that Maggie Smith should agree to accept $5,000 for any money found in or around the house. Mrs Smith thought this was very strange. She didn't sign it. In fact, she took Mr Jones to court. In court, Mr Jones told the truth: there wasn't $10,000. There was $150,000 in the walls, mainly in $50 or $100 notes. Joe Smith, Maggie's husband, was putting money in the wall for fifty years and he never told his wife. So what happened in the end? The judge decided that Maggie Smith should get all of the money. David Jones got nothing.

UNIT 8 Recording 3

Conversation 1

A: Hi there.

B: Hello.

A: Do you sell towels?

B: Towels? Yes, we should have some in the bathroom section. It's just over there past the clothes.

A: Great. Thanks very much.

Conversation 2

A: Good morning. Can I help you at all?

B: No, I'm just looking, thanks.

A: For anything in particular? We've got these new jeans. These are just in last week. Or we've got T-shirts here.

B: Um. OK, thanks.

A: Just let me know if you need any help.

Conversation 3

A: Excuse me. Have you got any of that stuff for killing insects?

B: Um, do you mean an insecticide? Like a spray?

A: Yes, a spray.

B: Hang on. We should have some … um. Give me a moment. I'll just check we've got some in stock. Yeah, we've got this one.

A: That looks fine.

Conversation 4

A: Who's next?

B: Hi.

A: Are you paying by cash or credit card?

B: Credit card. You take Visa, don't you?

A: Yeah, no problem. Can you enter your PIN, please? There you go.

B: Thanks.

A: Thanks. Bye.

UNIT 9 Recording 1

bigger than
smaller than
higher than
colder than
hotter than

UNIT 9 Recording 2

1 big … bigger … bigger than … The population in France is bigger than the population in Poland.
2 small … smaller … smaller than … France is smaller than Poland.
3 high … higher … higher than … Mont Blanc, in France, is higher than Rysy in Poland.
4 cold … colder … colder than … In January it is colder in Poland than in France.
5 hot … hotter … hotter than … In July it is hotter in France than in Poland.

UNIT 9 Recording 3

1 I'm lucky living by the sea. Every morning I see fishermen coming in after work. There's always something to do because the sea is always different. Every day you see something different. When I was younger we used to have parties and sleep on the beach. We cooked fish and listened to Bob Marley, and that was fun. These days I still go for walks every day with my dog. We've seen dolphins here. And we saw a dead whale on the beach once. It was enormous. It was on the beach for weeks.

2 As a child I played in a tree house in the garden. We were always outside. We invented games and we knew the names of animals and insects. We played in our garden or in our friends' gardens. It was very safe in those days. You could be outside all day. When I was young, we didn't have computers or even the television. And there wasn't as much crime, so we really grew up in the garden.

3 I go hiking and camping in the mountains. You can do that here in the summer. In the winter it's too cold. I think Americans like me enjoy the wild. We like big spaces, big skies. I'm just a few miles from a city, but there are all kinds of plants and animals out here. You can see deer and bears. It's pretty amazing.

4 I work with animals all the time. We have chickens, cows and pigs on the farm. There are a lot of farms around here, so it's completely normal to see animals around. I really like feeding the pigs 'cause they're quite funny to watch. One thing I don't like is getting up early. We do it every day. We get up at five in the morning and I'm always half asleep.

RC3 Recording 1

1 Could you help me?
2 Can you tell me where the office is?
3 Where can I find a post office?
4 What time does the library open?
5 When do the lessons start?

6 Is the swimming pool open on Sundays?

7 I need to speak to the director of studies.

UNIT 10 Recording 1

Conversation 1

A: What's your new teacher like?

B: She's really good. She makes the lessons interesting.

Conversation 2

A: What's it like living in the country?

B: It's a bit quiet. I think I preferred the city.

Conversation 3

A: Does your mother like staying with you?

B: She loves it. She comes to stay once a month.

Conversation 4

A: Do you like eating out in restaurants?

B: I enjoy it sometimes, but I prefer to cook at home.

Conversation 5

A: Is it much more expensive to live there now? What are the prices like?

B: It's not too bad. But it's more expensive than it was.

Conversation 6

A: Does your brother like it in Scotland?

B: He likes it a lot. He says it's beautiful.

Conversation 7

A: What's your new job like? Are you enjoying it?

B: It's brilliant. The people I work with are really friendly.

UNIT 10 Recording 2

1 What's your new teacher like?

2 What's it like living in the country?

3 Does your mother like staying with you?

4 Do you like eating out in restaurants?

5 What are the prices like?

6 Does your brother like it in Scotland?

7 What's your new job like?

UNIT 10 Recording 3

Conversation 1

S = Sophie   I = Interviewer

S: OK. Right. My name is Sophie Dunston and I'm sixteen years old. Well, one thing I don't like is people using their mobile phones or laptops or other technology at the wrong time.

I: What do you mean by the wrong time?

S: For example, during lessons. Or any time when someone's trying to talk to them.

I: Isn't this normal now?

S: I don't think so. Some of my friends don't even hear their parents because they spend their whole life wearing headphones. I think it's really rude.

I: And how would you stop this?

S: Well, in my school they banned personal technology during lessons and I think it was a really good idea. People can concentrate much better now.

Conversation 2

I = Interviewer   L = Luis

I: Luis, can you just introduce yourself briefly?

L: Yeah, I'm thirty-five years old and I'm a waiter. Shall I answer the questions?

I: Yes, go ahead.

L: OK. Well, for me the worst thing is litter.

I: On the street?

L: Litter on the street. People just throw away bits of paper or drop food. But it's also on the tube. I'm a Londoner. I go to work every day by tube and people just leave their newspapers lying around. And all this paper is a real mess.

I: How can we stop it?

L: I don't think you can stop it. The government has tried to introduce fines, but it hasn't worked.

I: What punishment would you suggest for people who drop litter?

L: I'd make them clean the streets.

Conversation 3

I = Interviewer   P = Pamela

I: If you just give your name and age ...

P: Alright. My name is Pamela and I'm seventy years old. But I think I'm a young seventy. Unlike most of my older friends, I love technology and I use email every day. But the one thing I hate about it is spam. It is so annoying. I think the people who are responsible should be forced to sit down and read millions of spam messages for six months.

I: That would teach them ...

P: Of course it would.

UNIT 10 Recording 4

1 There's a problem with my room.

2 Excuse me.

3 Could I speak to the manager?

4 Could you help me?

5 I'm afraid I have a problem.

6 I have to make a complaint.

UNIT 11 Recording 1

Conversation 1

A: Have you finished the book yet?

B: Yes, I've already started the next one.

Conversation 2

A: Have you cooked the dinner yet?

B: No, I've only just got home.

Conversation 3

A: Have you asked your wife yet?

B: No, I'm going to speak to her later.

Conversation 4

A: Have you decided where we're going yet?

B: Yes, we've just booked a table at Mario's.

Conversation 5

A: Do you want to come and play football?

B: No, I've already played twice this week.

Conversation 6

A: Have you seen Miranda?

B: Yes, she's just left.

UNIT 11 Recording 2

1 I get bored very easily. I prefer being busy, so I'm always doing things. Some people just like to sit down and do nothing. But I can't do that. I need to be active.

2 I feel lonely sometimes if my partner goes away for work and I'm on my own at home. But then I call a friend or my sister. Or I speak to someone who I haven't spoken to for a long time. Then I don't feel lonely anymore.

3 I get really confused when I have to do anything with numbers, like check bills or bank rates and things like that. I hate that kind of thing. I do find numbers confusing.

4 I am always amazed by nature. The beauty of nature. You can just stand in a beautiful place and look at it, and it's just amazing.

5 I get nervous when I have to organise a social event, like if I'm having a party or lots of people round to dinner. I get nervous about what I'm going to cook and if I'll have time to do everything.

6 I worry about all kinds of things. Often I feel worried about the world when I see the news and all the problems. There are so many problems in the world and a lot of the time I try not to think about them, and then suddenly, I'll start to worry.

UNIT 11 Recording 3

R = Robert   M = Miriam

R: I think they have already changed the way we live. I mean, a lot of people, like me, spend a lot of time playing on computer games. Some people already spend more time in virtual worlds, like Second Life, than they do in the real world. And I'm one of them. I'm starting to use Second Life at work too. I have meetings with my colleagues in Second Life. So, it's not just a game. I think people are starting to spend more and more time in virtual worlds where you can live in a castle by the beach and look beautiful, and fly, etc. It's more fun and exciting than the real world where you have to worry about money. So, yes, it started as a kind of game, but I think it's really changing how we live, how we work and study ... everything.

M: Well, they're not changing the way I live very much. I mean, they're just games like any other game. I quite like computer games, some of them. There are lots of games I don't like, like the violent games, but for me it's just the same as the other things I do. I mean, sometimes I read a book or watch television to relax. Sometimes I go out for a walk and sometimes I play a computer game. It's not changing my life. I don't spend all my time on the computer. I use a computer for work, so I don't want to be on the computer all the time at home too. And I think a lot of people are like me. In our free time we prefer to do other things.

UNIT 11 Recording 4

M = Manager   W = Worker

M: The project needs to be finished this week.

W: I'm afraid that's not possible.

M: Why not? Everything's possible.

W: I'm sorry, but I don't think it is. We're working hard, but we need another two weeks to finish the job.

M: Two weeks? Can you try to finish by the end of next week?

W: I'm really not sure about that. There's still a lot of work to do.

M: That's true. But you can get some more staff, so we can finish sooner. I'm sorry, but I don't see what the problem is.

W: I'm afraid I totally disagree. The problem is that we don't have more staff. We can't find people to start work tomorrow ...

UNIT 11 Recording 5

W = Worker   M = Manager

W: I'm afraid that's not possible.

W: I'm sorry, but I don't think it is.

W: I'm really not sure about that.

M: I'm sorry, but I don't see what the problem is.

W: I'm afraid I totally disagree.

UNIT 12 Recording 1

In the old days, big studios controlled their actors. This means they also controlled their actors' contracts. In fact, the studios had all the power. And they used this power to write some strange contracts. One example is Johnny Weissmuller, the swimmer who acted as Tarzan. As he got older, he got too fat. In his next role, the contract said he had to be one hundred and ninety pounds or less. If he came to work heavier than one hundred and ninety pounds, he lost $5,000 for every pound.

Another example is that of the silent film actor Buster Keaton who was famous for his sad face. The face became so important

that the studio said he could not smile on screen. And they wrote it in his contract: no smiling.

These days, of course, famous actors have all the power. They are the stars and their contracts show it. They ask for whatever they want. An example of this is Roger Moore, famous for playing James Bond. Mr Moore liked the good things in life. In his contract it was written that he could have an unlimited number of Cuban cigars. During one Bond film, the bill for his cigars was over £3,000.

Comedian Woody Allen agreed to act in a film by Disney. He asked the company to take his whole family for a private tour of Disneyland. They agreed and wrote it in his contract.

In her contract, Jennifer Lopez asked for a white changing room with white curtains and white sofas. The room also had to be full of white flowers. The contract also asked for lots of fresh food, including apple pie and ice cream.

Compared to actors, some musicians, especially rock stars, ask for very strange things in their contracts. The rock group Van Halen asked for plates full of the chocolate sweets M&Ms in their changing room. But they wanted all the brown ones removed. After that, The Rolling Stones' contract asked for all the brown M&Ms that Van Halen didn't eat. They were joking.

UNIT 12 Recording 2

celebration, politician
photographer, adventurous, celebrity
successful, musician, invention
dangerous, wonderful, scientist

UNIT 12 Recording 3

Conversation 1

A: Good afternoon. How can I help?

B: Hello. I'd like to go on a tour of the city.

A: OK. Are you thinking about a bus tour or private tour or boat tour?

B: A bus tour. Would you be able to recommend something?

A: Yes, we have regular tours throughout the day. The bus leaves every hour from outside the hotel.

B: Oh, perfect.

A: Here's some more information.

B: Thank you.

A: Would you like me to book you a seat? You don't have to. You can just wait outside the hotel if you like.

B: I'll just wait outside. Thanks very much.

A: You're welcome. Enjoy the tour.

Conversation 2

A: Excuse me. Would it be possible to change seats?

B: Umm, Let's have a look.

A: Are those seats free?

B: Yes, I think they are. Can you hold on a few minutes until they close the door?

A: Yes, of course.

B: Thanks.

Conversation 3

A: Hello.

B: Hello.

A: How are you?

B: Fine thanks.

A: Table for two?

B: Yes, please.

A: Did you book?

B: No.

A: OK, let me see what we've got. We're fairly busy, but we may have something. Just a moment. OK, We've got one free table. Would you come this way?

RC4 Recording 1

Conversation 1

A: Excuse me, could you help me?

B: Yes, of course. What can I do?

A: There's a problem with my key. It doesn't open the door.

B: I'm sorry about that. I'll get you another one.

Conversation 2

A: Excuse me, could I speak to the manager?

B: Yes. I'll just get him for you.

A: I'm afraid I have a complaint.

C: What seems to be the problem?

A: We still haven't had our main course.

C: I'm sorry but there's nothing we can do at the moment. We're very busy.

Conversation 3

A: Could you recommend a good place to go shopping?

B: Certainly. There's a new shopping centre not far from here. Would you like me to order you a taxi?

A: That would be great. Thank you.

B: No problem.

ANSWER KEY

UNIT 1

1.1

1

1 B 2 E 3 G 4 J 5 H 6 D 7 F
8 A 9 I 10 C

2

2 What time do your English lessons start?
3 How often do you cook for your friends?
4 How many people are there in your family?
5 Where does your mother come from?
6 Why don't you eat meat?
7 How many glasses of water do you drink in a day?
8 Where is the classroom?
9 When did you last see your best friend?
10 Where did you go shopping?

3

2 What do you do
3 Who do you live
4 How many people live with you/in the house
5 What do you do/like to do in your free time
6 How often do you go to the cinema
7 Why are you studying English
8 Which class are you in
9 When did you start learning English

4A

1 D 2 A 3 E 4 F 5 C 6 B

B

1 F 2 T 3 F 4 T 5 T 6 F

C

1 You should stand up and walk around.
2 Having good relationships makes you happy.
3 Things like answering a difficult email and making a dentist's appointment.
4 You will feel happy now because you will look forward to the special thing.
5 You will feel good/better.
6 When you smile, you feel better.

D

1 forward 2 relationships 3 Cross
4 touch 5 exercise

1.2

1

2 met, got on well 3 fell in love
4 asked her to marry him, accepted
5 got married 6 argued 7 got divorced 8 got back together again

2A

argue R happen R ask R decide R
find I get I know I look R meet I
say I spend I stay R study R
think I travel R

B

find – found get – got know – knew
meet – met say – said spend –
spent think – thought

3

1 met 2 got 3 started 4 became
5 lived 6 had 7 talked 8 sent
9 didn't tell 10 decided 11 arrived
12 asked

4

1 did you stay, found 2 ate 3 didn't have 4 went, didn't like, thought
5 spent 6 was, didn't have 7 wrote, didn't understand 8 gave 9 did you get 10 started, moved

5A/B

1 ended (ends in /ɪd/, the others end in /d/)
2 arrived (ends in /d/, the others end in /t/)
3 finished (ends in /t/, the others end in /ɪd/)
4 invented (ends in /ɪd/, the others end in /d/)
5 started (ends in /ɪd/, the others end in /t/)

6A

1 C 2 A 3 E 4 B 5 F 6 D

B

1 She was fourteen years old.
2 In Germany.
3 Elvis wrote letters and they spoke on the telephone.
4 In 1963 Priscilla moved to America.
5 She lived with Elvis's parents.
6 Priscilla started karate lessons and Mike was her teacher.
7 Yes, they stayed good friends.

7

2 We saw Pompeii and we thought it was wonderful.
3 She didn't like her job so she decided to leave.
4 They couldn't get married because her father wouldn't allow it.
5 He started taekwondo lessons because he wanted to get fit.
6 They wanted to buy the house but the bank didn't give them the money.
7 I bought a new computer but I'm having lots of problems with it.
8 I didn't sleep very well so I'm very tired today.

1.3

1

1 films 2 your health problems
3 your new computer 4 sport
5 your last holiday 6 the weather
7 politics 8 your work/studies

2

1 my friend 2 good weekend
3 isn't it 4 work here 5 Would you
6 Did you 7 do you 8 you know
9 meet you 10 in touch

3

2 Where‿are‿you going?
3 I come from‿Italy.
4 It's‿a beautiful day.
5 I'm‿afraid‿I can't remember.
6 Where did‿you buy‿it?
7 I'm sorry, but‿I don't‿understand.

4

1 Did you have a nice weekend?
2 Where did you go?
3 Would you like a drink?
4 So, do you like it here?
5 It was nice to meet you.
6 Let's keep in touch.

UNIT 2

2.1

1

1 company 2 colleague 3 staff
4 task 5 boss 6 employee 7 office
8 salary

Key word: customer

2

1 a ii, b i 2 a i, b ii 3 a ii, b i 4 a ii, b i
5 a ii, b i 6 a i, b ii

3

1 are you smiling 2 do you know
3 are they doing 4 are you drinking
5 Is he 6 She's wearing

4A

1 is 2 is working 3 doesn't like 4 is
5 is doing 6 is smiling 7 has 8 is
playing 9 is looking 10 are visiting

B

1 Julio 2 Bruce 3 Natasha 4 Amei
5 Hernan

5A

2 Things that companies do to
motivate their workers.

B

1 It is on the third and second floor
of the office.
2 They can go fishing.
3 On the last Friday of every month,
each department chooses a
theme and the workers dress up
accordingly.
4 They get a surprise trip and they
don't know where they're going.

C

1 pond 2 alternatives 3 uniform
4 fancy dress 5 monsters 6 trip

6A

1 Dear 2 about 3 hearing 4 Yours
sincerely 5 Hi 6 It's 7 See
8 Cheers

2.2

1

2 foreign correspondent 3 fashion
designer 4 IT consultant 5 rescue
worker 6 sales rep 7 personal
trainer

2A/B

6 syllables: foreign correspondent
5 syllables: fashion designer, IT
consultant, personal trainer
4 syllables: rescue worker
2 syllables: sales rep

3

2 team 3 pressure 4 salary
5 holidays 6 risk 7 with

4A

1 always 2 usually 3 never 4 Once
in a while 5 rarely 6 occasionally
7 never 8 always

5A

2 rarely happen 3 often happen
4 never happen

B

1 occasionally happen 2 always
happen 3 happen once in a while

6A

2 male elephant 3 pool 4 tour bus
5 tourists

B

1 Story 1 – a safari guide;
Story 2 – a tourist
2 Because an elephant charged at
them.
3 They escaped in the bus. No one
was injured.

C

3 Story 1 4 Story 2 5 Story 1
6 Story 2

D

1 b 2 a 3 a 4 b

2.3

1A

1 keen, absolutely 2 love, can't
3 on, mind 4 very, don't

C

1 chef 2 motorcycle courier 3 IT
consultant 4 accountant

2A

1 Do you like working in a team?
2 I can't stand working under
pressure.
3 I'm not very keen on my boss.
4 I don't like my colleagues.
5 I don't mind dealing with
customers.
6 Are you keen on sport?

B

1 f 2 e 3 a 4 b 5 c 6 d

3

2 works in the food industry
3 works in the fashion industry
4 works in education
5 works in sales and marketing
6 works in the tourist industry
7 works in the entertainment
industry
8 works in retail

4A

1 That sounds interesting, how does
it work
2 That's great, see, Right

3.1

1

2 get 3 go 4 see 5 get 6 have
7 go 8 go 9 have

2A

1 Are you going away on holiday this
year?
2 Who is cooking your dinner this
evening?
3 When are you going to the dentist?
4 What are you doing this weekend?
5 Are you going to play any sport this
week?
6 Are you going to marry Roberto?
7 What time are you meeting your
sister?
8 What are you going to do to
improve your English?
9 Are you having a party at the
weekend?
10 Are you going to the gym after
work?

B

1 f 2 a 3 e 4 h 5 g 6 c 7 b 8 d
9 j 10 i

3

1 are you doing, 'm staying
2 going to look 3 'm speaking
4 are meeting 5 Are you coming
6 are you going, 're going

4A

1 Van Gogh 2 Rembrandt
3 2,200 4 Thames 5 135 6 4,000
7 Serpentine 8 ninety

B

1 Nothing – they are free.
2 Eiffel Tower (Paris) and the Empire
State Building (New York)
3 You can see many of London's best
sights from here.
4 If it's raining, you won't see very
much at all.
5 There are over 4,000 trees and
many different types of birds and
butterflies.
6 play tennis, take a boat out on
the lake, go swimming, visit an art
gallery, go to a café/restaurant, go
to a concert or a protest
7 To take part in the Stop the War
protest.

5

Hi Mike,

I'm playing football later with a few of the boys from work. Would you like to **come**?

Dan

Dan,

I'm sorry, but **I'm** busy tonight. **I'm taking** Leila out for a meal. Wish me luck!

Thanks anyway.

Mike

Hi guys,

A few of us **are** going out for a curry on Friday night. Do you want **to** come with us? We're **meeting** at the Indian Tree at 8p.m.

Emma

Hi Emma,

I'd love to. See you there.

Jan

6A

1 I'm having a party
2 Do you want to come
3 We're going to have music
4 Julie is getting tickets to go to the theatre
5 We're going to see a Shakespeare play
6 Would you like to come

3.2

1

1 exhibition 2 paintings 3 art galleries 4 painter 5 artist 6 concert 7 rock 8 pop 9 jazz 10 bands 11 audience 12 performances

2

The wrong words are: 2 sculptures 3 concert hall 4 art gallery 5 concert 6 play 7 jazz 8 paintings 9 play 10 sculpture

3A

2 concert 3 paintings 4 composer 5 classical 6 sculptor 7 songwriter 8 exhibition 9 performance

4B

1 Terry doesn't like the painting.
2 It was expensive.
3 Mary is probably David's wife.

C

1 $45,000 2 no 3 yes

5A

1 What country 2 Which composer 3 Which painting 4 Who invented 5 Which French 6 What happens 7 Who wrote 8 What film 9 Who earned 10 Whose album 11 Whose life

B

1 i 2 g 3 c 4 d 5 a 6 h 7 e 8 b 9 f

6

2 What (music) was invented by African Americans in the USA?
3 Who brought the blues to the north in the early twentieth century?
4 Whose song *Laughing Song* (1895) was the first blues recording?
5 What music, originally from the Punjab region in India, has become world-famous?
6 Who first played bhangra music (to celebrate the spring)?
7 Whose album, *Folk and Funky* (1995), made bhangra music popular in the West?
8 What music mixes traditional Nigerian music with jazz and funk?
9 Who made Afrobeat famous?
10 Whose nightclub played Afrobeat for many years?

3.3

1A

A	R	R	A	N	G	E	V
C	A	N	C	E	L	M	O
H	B	Y	H	A	V	E	D
A	O	E	E	I	G	P	I
N	O	S	C	L	F	N	T
G	K	T	K	P	E	L	A
E	R	O	O	C	I	K	L
T	M	F	A	E	S	R	K

B

2 She called me because she wanted to **have** a chat.
3 Please **book** a table for us at the Blue Fin Restaurant tonight.
4 There's been a problem and I can't attend, so I'm calling to **cancel** my reservation.
5 I'd like to **check** some information: what time is the last train to Bern?
6 I'd like to come to the 4.30 performance, not the 6.30 one, and I'm calling to **change** my ticket.

7 The manager of Triad Books is on the phone. He wants to **talk** business.

2

1 e 2 d 3 g 4 c 5 f 6 b 7 a

3

A: Hello. ~~I'm~~ **It's/This is** Jim. Is Trudy there?
B: I'm afraid ~~but~~ she's not here at the moment.
A: Oh, really? Can I leave ~~the~~ **a** message?
B: Of course.
A: Can you tell her that we need to discuss the party on Friday?
B: Yes, I will. I'll ask her ~~for calling~~ **to call** you back.
A: Thanks a lot.
B: You're welcome. Bye.
A: Bye.

4

1 f 2 d 3 c 4 h 5 i 6 a 7 g 8 b 9 e 10 j

5

1 Can I just check? 2 I didn't catch that. 3 Can you repeat that? 4 can you speak up, please 5 can you slow down, please

6

1 tickets, after 6.00 2 station, 8.00 3 bookings, 8.00

REVIEW AND CHECK 1

1A

2 How 3 Where 4 Do 5 does 6 Do 7 Where 8 How 9 What

B

1 i 2 c 3 e 4 g 5 f 6 b 7 d 8 h 9 a

2A

get: married, the bus, on well
go: dancing, on holiday, to the cinema, sightseeing
have: children, time off work, a barbecue, dinner with someone
spend: money on clothes, time with someone

B

2 get the bus 3 spend time with someone 4 go dancing 5 go to the cinema 6 have a barbecue 7 get on well 8 go sightseeing 9 have dinner with someone

3

1 took   2 stayed   3 didn't tell   4 went
5 asked   6 complained   7 said
8 didn't get   9 didn't cook   10 told
11 talked   12 decided

4A

1 too   2 isn't, beautiful   3 So, come,
city   4 good weekend, time   5 would,
like, drink, love, water   6 nice, meet,
keep, touch

5

2 I ~~stay~~ 'm staying with some friends
for a few days so I can look for
somewhere to live.

3 I'~~m not knowing~~ don't know what
time the lesson starts.

4 They ~~spend~~ 're spending time with
their family in Germany at the
moment.

5 We'~~re~~ usually ~~going~~ out for a pizza
about once a week.

6 I'~~m not understanding~~ don't
understand where Jazz is. He never
arrives late.

7 ~~Do you watch~~ Are you watching
this programme? Or can I watch
the football on the other channel?

6

1 We always come here. It's the best
club in the area.

2 I hardly ever see her because she
works for a different company.

3 My parents occasionally help us
when we're busy.

4 I usually get up at about 6.30a.m.

5 Sal's very upset and says she never
wants to see him again.

6 Once in a while we go to
Scotland./We go to Scotland once
in a while.

7 I rarely have the chance to spend
time with my sister.

8 I take the children to school every
day./Every day I take the children
to school.

7

2 absolutely love   3 can't stand
4 doesn't like   5 don't mind   6 hates
7 like working   8 'm keen on

8

1 'm going shopping   2 is having   3 is
going to   4 're staying   5 Are you
coming   6 're flying

9

1 salary, boss   2 paintings, exhibition
3 work, pressure   4 audience   5 get,
long holidays   6 singer, songwriter
7 actor, Jazz   8 task

10A

2 Where **do** you come from?

3 correct

4 Why **did** David leave his job?

5 How often **do** you play football?

6 How much **does** it cost to fly to
Russia?

7 correct

8 correct

9 When **did** you last go to a concert?

10 correct

11 Why **are** you learning English?

12 Where **did** you buy that coat?

B

11 2 d   3 f   4 h   5 g   6 b   7 a   8 j
9 i   10 c   11 e   12 k

TEST

1 b   2 a   3 c   4 b   5 c   6 a   7 b   8 b
9 c   10 a   11 c   12 b   13 a   14 b
15 a   16 b   17 c   18 a   19 c   20 b
21 c   22 a   23 b   24 b   25 c   26 a
27 c   28 b   29 a   30 c

UNIT 4

4.1

1A

1 make   2 do   3 do   4 make   5 make
6 do   7 make   8 do   9 do   10 make
11 do   12 make   13 do   14 make

B

3 I made a phone call.

4 I did a lot of sport.

5 I made a mistake.

6 I made a meal.

7 I did a project.

8 I did my homework.

9 I made a speech.

10 I made an appointment.

11 I did business.

12 I did well.

2

1 b   2 b   3 a   4 a   5 b   6 a   7 a   8 b

3

2 have made   3 Have you ever spent
4 went   5 laughed   6 has spent
7 haven't had   8 watched   9 have
never eaten

4A

Gordon Ramsay: chef, football;

Winston Churchill: politician (prime
minister), writer;

Woody Allen: actor/director; clarinet
player

B

1 T   2 T   3 F   4 F   5 F

C

1 a   2 b   3 b   4 a

5

The Greatest Mind in Fiction

Most of fiction's great minds ~~belongs~~
belong (gr) either to criminals or
to the men and women who catch
them. ~~A~~ **The (gr)** greatest of these
is probably Sherlock Holmes. The
Holmes stories were written by Sir
Arthur Conan Doyle, **(p)** a ~~docter~~
doctor (sp) from ~~edinburgh~~ **Edinburgh
(p)**, Scotland. Conan Doyle knew a
lot about the human body and ~~pollice~~
police (sp) work, and he ~~has~~ **(gr)** used
this information in his books. Very
quickly, Conan Doyle's hero ~~beccame~~
became (sp) popular. When Holmes
was killed in one story, thousands
of readers protested. Conan Doyle
changed his mind, and Holmes
appeared in another story. **(p)**

4.2

1

Across: 4 test   7 piano   8 sport
10 online   11 take

Down: 1 mistakes   2 performance
3 study   5 languages   6 uniform
9 play

2

1 2 don't have to   3 can   4 Can
5 can't   6 Can   7 can   8 have to
9 can

2 1 have to   2 have to   3 have to
4 don't have   5 can   6 can   7 Can
8 can

3A

1 do I have to   2 Can I   3 We must
4 We don't have to   5 She can't
6 You mustn't

4A

1 You **can't have** your mobile phone
switched on.

2 You have to register before **you can**
use the site.

3 I'm afraid **she can't** speak to you at
the moment.

4 **You can** use my computer if you
want to.

B

1 **You have to/must be** good at
foreign languages if you want to
learn Mandarin.

2 **We have to/must be** there on time,
or they won't let us in.

3 **We don't have to** have a licence to fish here.

4 **You mustn't** tell him I'm here.

5

2 can't   3 must/have to   4 can
5 can't/mustn't   6 have to   7 can
8 must/have to   9 can't   10 Can
11 can't/mustn't

6A

Picture A: holist – learns lots of information about a topic, but in no particular order

Picture B: serialist – learns things in sequence from the bottom up

B

1 S   2 S   3 H   4 S   5 H

C

1 b   2 a   3 a

4.3

1

1 memorise   2 look (it) up   3 reread
4 chat   5 subtitles   6 visit (English) websites

2

1 Try talking about films   2 I don't think you should   3 Why don't you try   4 I don't think it's a good idea
5 I think you should get   6 Why don't you buy   7 I think you should try
8 It's a good idea to think

3

1 I think you should   2 Why don't you/Why not   3 It's a good idea to   4 Try talking   5 I don't think it's a good idea to   6 Why don't you try
7 I think you should   8 It's a good idea to

4A

a suppose   b You're   c a good   d so
e sure that's   f right

B

1 c   2 f   3 e   4 a   5 b   6 d

UNIT 5

5.1

1A

ship   motorbike   tram   moped   aeroplane   lorry   speedboat   helicopter   coach   ferry   hot air balloon   underground   minibus

B

2 lorry   3 coach   4 minibus
5 aeroplane   6 helicopter   7 hot

air balloon   8 ship   9 speedboat
10 ferry   11 motorbike   12 moped
13 tram   14 underground

C

1 taxi   2 underground   3 hot air balloon   4 coach   5 lorry
6 motorbike/moped   7 speedboat
8 ship

2

1 g   2 f   3 c   4 a   5 d   6 h   7 b   8 e

3

1 was playing, didn't hear

2 did it happen, was climbing, landed

3 saw, was studying, said

4 Were you driving, was going, came

5 saw, were you going, was going, dropped

4A

1 drop his ticket   2 pay the taxi driver
3 go through security   4 go for a walk
5 try to sleep   6 decide to use his mobile phone

B

2 was paying the taxi driver

3 was going through security

4 went for a walk

5 were trying to sleep

6 decided to use

6A

A

B

1 T   2 T   3 F   4 F   5 F   6 T

7B

1 he typed the wrong destination on a travel website

2 it was very small

3 his parents and friends from Germany sent him some money

5.2

1A

Across: 3 digital camera   7 notebook
8 sunhat   9 suitcase

Down: 2 walking boots   4 souvenirs
5 binoculars   6 money belt

B

2 souvenirs   3 sunhat   4 walking boots   5 waterproof clothes
6 binoculars   7 money belt   8 suitcase
9 digital camera

2

1 reading   2 to see   3 to get
4 spending   5 to rain   6 to refund
7 travelling   8 to finish   9 to see
10 writing   11 living   12 going

3

2 I expect to hear from the travel agent later today.

3 We want to go on holiday but we're too busy.

4 We seem to go back to the same place every year.

5 Alan chose to stay in a hotel.

6 We enjoy walking and looking at the beautiful countryside.

7 I decided to travel on my own.

8 We avoid visiting tourist resorts in (the) summer.

9 We need to book our flights before (the) prices go up.

4A

a 4   b 1 or 2   c 3   d 1   e 2

B

2 review   3 locations   4 skills   5 edit
6 hostels

C

1 3   2 4   3 1, 2 or 4   4 1   5 2

5A

Story 1: a, b, h d

Story 2: g, f, i, e, c

5.3

1

2 b   3 c   4 a   5 f   6 d   7 e

2

1 on   2 along   3 through   4 –   5 at
6 of   7 –   8 past

3

2 bar   3 university hall   4 theatre
5 park   6 library

4A

1 Can you help me, You can't miss it, Can you show me on the map

2 Is this the right way, You'll see it in front of you, Can I walk, It takes about ten minutes

3 Is it far, So I need to go left at the cinema

UNIT 6

6.1

1

1 fresh   2 junk   3 exercise   4 walking
5 life   6 working   7 stressed   8 frozen
9 miss   10 caffeine   11 fizzy

2

1 has been

2 have (ever) watched

3 has gone, haven't seen

4 Have (you) finished, haven't started

5 has arrived

6 Have (you) found

7 have (you) known, haven't been

8 Have (you) heard, Have (you) decided

3

2 He's worked for that company for six months.

3 We've lived in Turkey since 2006.

4 I haven't been to the cinema for a long time.

5 They've been here for two months now.

6 I haven't cleaned the house since last Monday.

7 She hasn't listened to that music since she was a teenager.

8 We haven't heard from him since he left.

9 Bob has been a builder for more than forty years.

10 The phone hasn't rung since 10 o'clock.

11 I've wanted to climb a mountain since I was a child.

4

1 did you start 2 did you want
3 started 4 felt 5 have lived 6 I've had 7 I've worked 8 travelled
9 met 10 I have ever seen 11 have used 12 have become

5A

1 a 2 b 3 a 4 a 5 a

6A

1 c 2 a 3 b

B

1 F 2 T 3 F 4 T 5 F 6 F

C

1 c 2 e 3 a 4 b 5 d

6.2

1

mango plum grape apple orange lemon melon

note 'pear' is also possible, but this does not appear in the Students' Book

2

1 chicken 2 bacon 3 broccoli
4 Beefsteak 5 spinach 6 potatoes
7 leg of lamb 8 cabbage
9 courgettes 10 shrimps 11 onions
12 garlic 13 mussels 14 cheese

3

1 a 2 c 3 c 4 a 5 b 6 a 7 c 8 b

4

2 We won't eat animals in the future.

3 We may eat more organic food.

4 Junk food might become illegal.

5 People will get fatter in the West.

6 There may not be any fish left in the sea.

5A

1 C 2 D 3 B 4 A

B

1 b 2 b 3 a 4 a 5 b 6 b

C

1 concentrating 2 variety
3 experiments 4 on average

6A

1 I have always liked cooking **and** I cook every day.

2 I was very young **when** I cooked my first meal.

3 I don't eat much meat **but** I eat a lot of fish.

4 I was working as a chef in a horrible hotel **when** I decided to open my own restaurant.

5 I don't drink alcohol **but** I (do) use a little wine in some of the dishes I prepare.

6 I like meeting customers at my restaurant **and** I ask them about the food.

B

1 My favourite types of food are pasta **and** fresh fish. I **also** like fruit.

2 Every morning I buy vegetables **and** herbs from the market. I **also** buy meat there.

3 I find that the food in the market is fresher **and** better quality. It's **also** cheaper.

6.3

1

Across 5 painkillers 7 broken
9 antibiotics 10 X-ray

Down 1 medicine 2 cold 3 rest
4 temperature 6 headache 8 sore

2

Doctor

1 e 2 c 3 a 4 f 5 d 6 b

Patient

7 k 8 j 9 h 10 g 11 i

3A

Conversation 1

Doctor: Your leg? What's **the** matter with it?

Woman: Well, **it's** very painful. It hurts when I walk.

Doctor: I see. How long have you **had** the problem?

Woman: Since yesterday. ✔

Doctor: Can I **have** a look?

Woman: Yes, of course. ✔

Conversation 2

Doctor: Hello. What's **the** matter, Mr Smith?

Man: I feel terrible. ✔

Doctor: All right. Where does **it** hurt?

Man: Everywhere. And **I** can't sleep.

Doctor: Ah. Have you got **a** temperature?

Man: I don't know. ✔

Doctor: OK. Can I have **a** look?

Man: Yes, of course. ✔

Doctor: That's fine. It's nothing **to** worry about.

Man: But I feel terrible! ✔

4A

Conversation 1

1 What's the matter

2 How long have you had the problem

3 Have you got a temperature/Do you have a temperature

4 you've got a cold

5 plenty of rest

6 hot drinks

Conversation 2

1 Can I have a look

2 Where does it hurt

3 How did you do it

4 go to hospital for an X-ray

REVIEW AND CHECK 2

1

2 have never visited 3 came
4 Have (you ever) seen 5 have been
6 got 7 did (you) go 8 haven't met
9 didn't hear 10 has never won
11 has (she) ever eaten

2

1 a 2 c 3 c 4 b 5 a 6 a 7 c 8 b
9 b 10 c

3

2 Should 3 shouldn't 4 suppose
5 sure 6 think 7 idea 8 Why

4

1 happened 2 was studying 3 was sitting 4 saw 5 realised 6 wasn't looking 7 didn't help 8 had 9 was watching 10 received

5

2 I want **to write** a great book so I can become famous!

3 I need **to get up** early tomorrow so I'm going to bed now.

4 We usually avoid **driving** at this time because of all the traffic.

5 Do you enjoy **cooking** meals for large groups of people?

6 They decided **to clean** the whole house after the party.

7 She loves **shopping** for clothes.

8 I always seem **to lose** something when I travel – usually my plane ticket.

6

I g 2 d 3 c 4 e 5 f 6 b 7 a 8 h

7

The incorrect alternatives are: I since ten minutes 2 since months
3 for January 4 since years 5 for the last meal 6 for now 7 since months
8 for December 9 since two years

8

I I ~~don't will~~ **won't** go to the cinema tonight because I'm busy.

2 I may ~~to~~ send her an email.

3 We ~~not might~~ **might not** have time to go to the museum.

4 The weather report on TV said there might ~~to~~ be storms.

5 Joshua may not ~~be~~ go to the game.

6 I'~~m~~ might be late to class tonight.

9A

a D b P c D d P e P f D

B

I c 2 e 3 a 4 f 5 b 6 d

10

I appointment 2 binoculars
3 caffeine 4 decision 5 exam
6 fizzy 7 games 8 homework
9 information technology 10 junk
food II kit 12 literature
13 motorbike/moped 14 native
speaker 15 online 16 pill
17 rucksack 18 souvenir 19 tram
20 uniform 21 vegetables
22 waterproof 23 yoga

TEST

I c 2 a 3 b 4 b 5 a 6 a 7 c
8 c 9 a 10 b II c 12 b 13 b
14 c 15 a 16 c 17 b 18 c 19 b
20 c 21 a 22 c 23 b 24 c 25 c
26 a 27 b 28 b 29 a 30 c

UNIT 7

7.1

I

I up, around 2 to, for 3 about, back
4 about, for

2

I c 2 e 3 f 4 g 5 a 6 b 7 d

3

2 used to read 3 Did (you) use to study 4 used to be 5 Did (you) use to spend 6 used to stay 7 used to run 8 didn't use to like 9 didn't use to come

4

2 They used to dream about a life on the beach.

3 They used to sit in traffic on the way to the office.

4 Harry used to wear a suit to go to work.

5 James didn't use to spend his time sitting on the beach.

6 They didn't use to eat tropical fruit for breakfast.

7 They didn't use to wear shorts and a T-shirt to work.

8 They didn't use to go surfing at the end of the day.

9 James's colleagues used to think he was crazy.

5A

I used to be 2 didn't use to have
3 used to give 4 used to study
5 used to live 6 use to go

6

I B 2 D 3 C 4 A 5 F 6 E

7

I F 2 F 3 T 4 T 5 F 6 F

8

Set new goals

I What exactly do you want to change in your life?

2 Decide on some new goals to help you achieve this change and write them down.

3 Writing down your goals is the first step towards achieving them.

Do something different

I Do you spend a lot of your time doing the same things every day?

2 Try not doing something for a while (like not watching television for one week).

3 This will give you time to try doing something different.

Think about now

I Don't spend too much time thinking about the past and worrying about decisions you have already made.

2 And don't worry about things which haven't happened yet.

3 If you try to focus on the present, things will seem easier.

Learn a new skill

I Learning a new skill might give you new opportunities in life.

2 Also the process of learning something new will make you feel better and more satisfied.

3 So, if you learn a new skill, you'll find you can quickly get out of a rut.

7.2

I

2 documentary 3 saves 4 became
5 arrested 6 spend 7 role

2

Not possible: 2 film 3 many people
4 a theatre 5 a long way 6 a play
7 thief

3

I I worked hard ~~for~~ to pass my exams.

2 correct

3 I play a lot of sport because **I** want to stay fit.

4 He drove for six hours to ~~meeting~~ **meet** you.

5 The bus was late so ~~that~~ we walked.

6 I spent time abroad because ~~of~~ I like travelling.

7 I'm going to the restaurant ~~for~~ **to** meet my friends.

8 correct

9 I went to the shop ~~for buying~~ **to buy** the book.

10 I live miles from my office ~~but~~ **so** I get a train to work.

4

I because, so 2 Because, So 3 To, so 4 so, to

5A

I c 2 a 3 a 4 c 5 b 6 b

B

I divorced 2 religion 3 remember
4 country 5 actor 6 mistake

C

1 get divorced   2 lead singer   3 to identify with   4 birth certificate
5 immigrant   6 boxer   7 to separate

D

1 birth certificate   2 identify with
3 give (an) example   4 real name
5 got divorced   6 lead singer

7.3

1

Across: 6 cafeteria   8 lecture
9 library   10 book shop

Down: 1 photocopying room
2 registration desk   3 welfare office
4 main reception   5 stationery shop
7 classroom

2

1 library   2 reception   3 Thank
4 kind   5 know   6 Sorry   7 cafeteria
8 opens   9 Thank   10 help   11 tell
12 Sorry   13 Can   14 here
15 classroom   16 Thank

3

2 leave it/my bag
3 you say 9 o'clock
4 (You need to buy) a notebook
5 Sorry (, can you say that again, please)
6 you say in the lecture theatre

UNIT 8

8.1

1

2 cash   3 lend   4 bill   5 borrow
6 notes   7 coins   8 tip   9 earn
10 invest   11 worth

2

1 b   2 c   3 a   4 c   5 a   6 c   7 a
8 b   9 b   10 c

3

2 who fixed my teeth
3 where you get free food
4 that/which I left on your table
5 that/which sells old CDs
6 that I gave to your girlfriend
7 who helped me get fit
8 where I was born
9 who introduced me to your sister

4

2 It's a place **where** you can really relax.
3 Do you still see your friend who ~~she~~ became a motorcycle courier?
4 Clarissa started a company that ~~it~~ sells organic food.
5 correct
6 That's the house ~~that~~ **where** I was born.
7 I don't like people ~~which~~ **who** talk all the time.
8 correct
9 Is this the iPod that you want ~~it~~?

5B

1 Junichi Inamoto   2 Marlon Brando
3 Chanel No. 5   4 J K Rowling

C

1 fans   2 nickname   3 lines
4 billionaire   5 magic

6A

Hanser Lightman six-string acoustic guitar: €45

The guitar is in **very** good condition.

The previous owner used it for only two months, and it plays **perfectly**.

We can ship it to you **quickly** – within 24 hours.

This is a **really** good offer for a beginner.

The guitar is **extremely** easy to play.

8.2

1

1 took up   2 took it back   3 give it back   4 gave in   5 give up   6 took over

2

1 up   2 in   3 back   4 up   5 over
6 back

4

2 enough/much – Melanie   3 much – Sandra   4 enough – Doris   5 too – Melanie
6 very – Melanie   7 many – Doris
8 much – Melanie   9 many – Sandra
10 too – Doris

5

1 a ii, b i   2 a ii, b i   3 a ii, b i   4 a i, b ii
5 a i, b ii   6 a ii, b i   7 a i, b ii   8 a i, b ii

6B

Maggie and Joe Smith lived in the same house for ~~fifteen~~ **fifty** years. When Joe died, Maggie sold the house to David Jones. A few ~~years~~ **weeks** later, Maggie heard someone say that Jones had found some money in her old house. Jones told her there was $10,000 in the wall. He offered her $5,000. She agreed. A few days later, Jones asked Maggie to sign a contract that said she should accept $5,000 for any money found in ~~the garden~~ **or around the** house. She didn't sign it. Instead, she took Jones to court. In court, he told the truth: there wasn't $10,000. There was ~~$15,000~~ **$150,000**. Joe Smith, Maggie's husband, was putting money in the wall for fifty years and he never told his wife. In the end, the judge decided that ~~Mr Jones~~ **Maggie** should get all of the money.

8.3

1

1 customer   2 label   3 brand
4 supermarket   5 online   6 butcher

hidden word: market

2

1 A: Can I help you?
   B: I'm just looking, thanks.
2 A: Are you looking for anything in particular?
   B: Do you sell hats?
3 A: Do you have one of these in a larger size?
   B: I'll just have a look.
4 A: Can I try these on?
   B: Yes, the room fitting is here.
5 A: Are you paying by cash or credit card?
   B: By credit card.
6 A: Can you enter your PIN?
   B: Yes, of course.

3

1 cash   2 PIN   3 sign   4 particular
5 fit   6 size   7 looking   8 Can

4

1 things   2 stuff   3 a type   4 a kind of

5A

1 C   2 D   3 B   4 A

B

1 towels   2 new jeans and T-shirts
3 yes   4 credit card (Visa)

UNIT 9

9.1

1

1 b   2 b   3 a   4 b   5 b   6 a

2

2 Poland is smaller than France.
3 Mont Blanc, in France, is higher than Rysy in Poland.
4 In January, it is colder in Poland than in France.
5 In July, it is hotter in France than in Poland.

3A

b

4

1 the coldest 2 worse 3 the most popular 4 cheaper 5 longer 6 hotter 7 shorter 8 better 9 the longest 10 happier 11 the funniest 12 more difficult

5

1, 2 and 4

6

1 He thinks it helps people who work in the city to relax.
2 They can learn about organic gardening and recycling.
3 His father gave it to him.
4 They eat some of it, and sell some at the market.
5 It's a house in the country (sometimes it's a very small house).
6 They can enjoy fresh air and growing their own vegetables.

7

1 Is this ~~you're~~ **your** coat?
2 They gave us ~~there~~ **their** car for the weekend.
3 Have you got an extra ticket? I'd like to come ~~to~~ **too**.
4 We spent the weekend by the ~~see~~ **sea**.
5 Do you know ~~wear~~ **where** the office is?
6 Are you sure this is the ~~write~~ **right** way?

8

1 your 2 it's 3 too 4 sea 5 their 6 right

9.2

1A

F	E	A	T	U	R	E	S	C
N	D	E	R	F	S	G	C	O
A	I	R	O	Y	Z	A	E	R
T	S	T	P	A	R	K	N	U
U	D	E	I	F	C	X	E	R
R	S	F	C	O	P	L	R	A
A	D	N	A	M	E	W	Y	L
L	W	I	L	D	L	I	F	E

B

1 features 2 air 3 park 4 scenery 5 wildlife 6 tropical 7 rural 8 natural

C

1 fresh air 2 rural area 3 wildlife centre 4 geographical features 5 tropical rainforest 6 national park 7 beautiful scenery 8 natural beauty

2

2 the weather 3 elephants – 4 an architect 5 the camera 6 Europe – 7 January – 8 a doctor 9 the sun 10 Thursday – 11 the noise

3

2 – 3 a/the 4 a 5 – 6 a 7 the 8 – 9 an 10 a 11 the

4A

a Speaker 2 b Speaker 4 c Speaker 1 d Speaker 3

B

1a goes for walks 1b (dead) whale 2a animals and insects 2b in the garden 3a in the summer 3b spaces, skies 4a chickens, cows, pigs 4b getting up early

C

1 d 2 g 3 f 4 h 5 a 6 e 7 b 8 c

D

1 completely normal 2 be outside 3 fun 4 all kinds of 5 hiking 6 tree house 7 feeding 8 enormous

9.3

1

1 camel 2 shark 3 dolphin 4 mosquito 5 penguin 6 whale 7 snake 8 zebra 9 tortoise 10 monkey

hidden word: chimpanzee

2

1 That animal might ~~to~~ be a chimpanzee or a monkey.
2 correct
3 The waterfall ~~don't can~~ **can't** be here – it's too dry.
4 correct
5 They must ~~be~~ have a dog – look at all the hair on the sofa!
6 The mountain range in the picture could ~~to~~ be the Himalayas.
7 correct
8 That's definitely ~~no~~ **not** a mosquito bite – it's too big.

3

1 might, could 2 perhaps, might 3 must, maybe 4 might, could

4

1 Well 2 That's a good question 3 It's hard to say 4 Let me think 5 I'm not sure

REVIEW AND CHECK 3

1

2 didn't use 3 to drink 4 use to 5 she use 6 to play 7 Did your 8 used to 9 to use

2

2 because 3 so 4 so 5 to 6 because 7 to 8 so 9 to 10 to 11 so 12 because

3

1 Could you help me?
2 Can you tell me where the office is?
3 Where can I find a post office?
4 What time does the library open?
5 When do the lessons start?
6 Is the swimming pool open on Sundays?
7 I need to speak to the director of studies.

4

1 cure 2 spent, travel 3 room, back 4 desk, for 5 documentary, moves 6 with, lecture

5

2 that/which we drove to California
3 where my son was born
4 that/which designs computer systems for businesses
5 who was working as a model
6 where you work quietly or borrow books

6

1 much 2 enough 3 very 4 too 5 many 6 much 7 enough

7A/B

1 Excuse me. Do you ~~to~~ sell binoculars? C
2 Do you have one **of** these in a larger size? C
3 Are you looking for anything in ~~particularly~~ **particular**? S
4 It ~~isn't fitting~~ **doesn't fit** me. C
5 Are you paying by cash or ~~the~~ credit card? S
6 Can you just ~~to~~ sign here, please? S
7 Where's the ~~fit~~ **fitting** room? C

8

1 lend 2 notes 3 invest in 4 take over 5 give up 6 market 7 customer service

9

1 Elephants are bigger than lions.
2 Gold is more expensive than silver.
3 This is the worst weather for many years.

4 Russia is the biggest country in the world.

5 A Mercedes is more expensive than a Toyota.

6 It's the most exciting film I've ever seen.

10

2 an 3 a 4 – 5 The 6 – 7 the
8 the 9 the 10 – 11 a 12 an 13 a
14 the 15 the 16 –

11

not possible: 2 I definitely will 3 it must be 4 can't 5 it can't be

12

natural places/the outdoors: fresh air, ocean, coastline, geographical features, wildlife centre, lake

land animals: monkey, cheetah, bear

animals that fly: pigeon, eagle, mosquito

animals that live in water: whale, dolphin, shark

TEST

1 c 2 c 3 a 4 b 5 a 6 c 7 a 8 b
9 c 10 a 11 c 12 b 13 c 14 b
15 c 16 a 17 a 18 c 19 b 20 a
21 b 22 c 23 c 24 b 25 c 26 a
27 b 28 c 29 c 30 a

UNIT 10

10.1

1

1 traffic 2 crowded 3 clean, safe
4 nightlife 5 things to see (and) do
6 public transport system 7 crime
8 friendly, polite 9 green spaces
10 buildings

2

1 buildings 2 public transport
3 traffic 4 friendly/helpful, polite
5 nice parks/green spaces 6 crime
7 polluted 8 crowded 9 nightlife
10 clean, safe

3

1 it like 2 you like 3 do you like
4 like 5 she like 6 What's (the weather) like 7 Do you like 8 is (that new restaurant by the river) like

4

2 What's it ~~to~~ like living in the country?

3 Does your mother **like** staying with you?

4 ~~Are~~ **Do** you like eating out in restaurants?

5 Is it much more expensive to live there now? What **are** the prices like?

6 ~~Do~~ **Does** your brother like it in Scotland?

7 ~~Which's~~ **What's** your new job like? Are you enjoying it?

5

1 Paris 2 Asunción 3 a

6

1 Yes, they think Vienna, Prague and Venice are also romantic.

2 It's very crowded.

3 Yes, they are always at the top of the list.

4 No, they are not.

5 No, it was once one of the most dangerous cities in the world.

6 They are some of the best restaurants in the world.

7

1 picnic 2 go by 3 capital 4 title
5 once 6 sights

8

1 Dear Mr Smith,

2 I am writing to ask about courses at your college.

3 I'd like to know what courses you have in August.

4 In addition to this, I would like to know the prices.

5 I look forward to hearing from you soon.

6 Yours sincerely, Sally Bridges

10.2

1

2 judge, prison sentence 3 shoplifters, steal 4 criminal, victim 5 fine, writing graffiti 6 Community service, fraud
7 arrested, shoplifting 8 investigating, theft 9 breaks, shoots

2

1 d 2 h 3 b 4 c 5 g 6 a 7 e 8 f

3

1 is killed 2 are called 3 is looked at
4 bring 5 is discovered 6 is found
7 miss 8 do

4

1 was arrested 2 was told 3 came
4 was caught 5 had 6 said 7 was given 8 chose

5

1 are given extra homework every day

2 does not sell his books

3 destroyed the library

4 wasn't eaten (by the children)

5 is used in hundreds of products

6 caught the thief

7 weren't told about the exam

8 are not found in Africa

6A

Sophie talks about technology.

Luis talks about litter.

Pamela talks about spam.

B

1 c 2 b 3 a 4 c 5 c 6 c

7

1 rude 2 banned 3 litter 4 lying around 5 mess 6 fines 7 annoying

10.3

1

Across: 1 delay 4 spam 5 service
7 faulty

Down: 2 litter 3 crash 4 stuck
6 virus

2

1 a 2 c 3 b 4 c 5 b 6 c

3A

1 There's a problem with the printer.

2 The microphone doesn't work.

3 I've been here for over two hours.

B

a 3 b 1 c 2

4A

2 Excuse 3 Could 4 help 5 afraid
6 complaint

UNIT 11

11.1

1

1 mobile 2 blog 3 send 4 email
5 text 6 chat 7 webpage 8 internet

2

1 I haven't finished packing yet.

2 I've already spoken to her.

3 Yes, we've just got back from holiday.

4 Yes, but I haven't watched it yet.

5 I've just got my exam results.

6 But I've already spent all my money.

3

1 have just woken up 2 have just finished 3 have just eaten
4 has just lost 5 has just passed
6 have just heard 7 has just sent
8 has just stopped 9 has just arrived
10 have just started

4

2 A: Have you cooked the dinner yet?

   B: No, I've only just got home.

3 A: Have you asked your wife yet?

4 A: Have you decided where we're going yet?

   B: Yes, we've just booked a table at Mario's.

5 B: No, I've already played twice this week.

6 A: Have you seen Miranda?

   B: Yes, she's just left.

5

b

6

1 T 2 F 3 T 4 F 5 F 6 T

7

1 post 2 stingy 3 blogger
4 strong opinions 5 armchair
6 teenagers/the younger generation

8

2 I took ~~my grandmother~~ **her** out to lunch.

3 I hadn't seen ~~my friends~~ **them** for a long time.

4 He's enjoying ~~the new job~~ **it**.

5 Then he gave ~~Mark and me~~ **us** the bill.

6 I'd like to stay ~~in this place~~ **here** for ever.

11.2

1

1 excited 2 confused
3 uncomfortable 4 nervous 5 lonely
6 worried 7 amazed 8 bored

2

1 b 2 e 3 a 4 c 5 f 6 d

3

1 d 2 f 3 c 4 h 5 a 6 g 7 b 8 e

4

1 am, will be 2 will call, is 3 see, will tell 4 doesn't come, will be 5 get, will earn 6 will buy, are 7 will change, see 8 will, do, lose

5

1 wait 2 will be 3 go 4 have 5 stay
6 will spend 7 go 8 won't know
9 look 10 find 11 get 12 will, look

6

2 If the elephant walks on the bridge, the bridge will break.

3 If the bridge breaks, the elephant will fall.

4 If the elephant falls, the crocodiles will eat it.

5 If the man falls, his girlfriend will scream.

6 If the girlfriend screams, the snake will wake up.

7 If the snake wakes up, it will bite the girlfriend.

8 If the man doesn't cross the bridge, he can keep the flowers.

9 If he keeps flowers, it will be a lot easier.

7

Robert: 1 Yes 2 Yes 3 Yes 4 Yes
Miriam: 1 No 2 Yes 3 Yes 4 No

8

1 changed 2 time 3 colleagues
4 money 5 violent 6 computer
7 me 8 prefer

11.3

1

1 blog 2 search engines 3 message boards 4 social networking sites
5 travel websites 6 online news
7 music download 8 video sharing

2

1 don't 2 my 3 Definitely 4 That's
5 sure 6 totally 7 true

3

1 I'm sorry, but I don't think that's right.

2 I'm afraid I totally disagree.

3 I'm really not sure about that.

4 I'm sorry, but I don't think so.

4A

To make the phrases more polite, add *I'm sorry,* and *I'm afraid.*

B

1 I'm afraid that's not possible.

2 I'm sorry, but I don't think it is.

3 I'm really not sure about that.

4 I'm sorry, but I don't see what the problem is.

5 I'm afraid I totally disagree.

UNIT 12

12.1

1

2 musical 3 comedy 4 documentary
5 horror film 6 action film 7 science fiction film 8 fantasy film 9 thriller
10 western

2

2 a ✗, b ✔ 3 a ✔, b ✗ 4 a ✗, b ✔
5 a ✗, b ✔ 6 a ✗, b ✔

3

1 h 2 c 3 j 4 g 5 e 6 i 7 a 8 b
9 d 10 f

4

2 he was starring in a TV series

3 he would appear in a film the following year

4 the film was called *Samba Nights*

5 he could work with any Hollywood directors he chose

6 he was living in Beverly Hills

7 he was getting married to Sonia Jeffers the following month

8 me she was a famous actor too

9 he would text me the following week

10 he could take me to some great parties

5A

2 190 3 smile 4 actors 5 family
6 contracts

B

1 He was too fat. 2 over £3,000
3 white 4 chocolate sweets (M&Ms)

C

1 d 2 a 3 e 4 b 5 c

D

1 changing room 2 on screen 3 star
4 role 5 studio

12.2

1

2 successful 3 celebration
4 adventurous 5 politicians
6 photographer 7 wonderful
8 dangerous 9 helpful

2

ooOo: 1 politician

oOoo: 2 adventurous 3 celebrity

oOo: 4 musician 5 invention

Ooo: 6 wonderful 7 scientist

3

1 didn't have, wouldn't be

2 didn't have, would love

3 would be, didn't argue

4 would ask, needed

5 didn't rain, would go out

6 wouldn't be, went

7 had, would offer

8 was able to/could, would move

4

1 If I were famous, people would recognise me on the street.
2 If she had more money, she would buy a car.
3 What would you do if you lost your job?
4 If I lost my job, I would have to look for another one.
5 I would travel to China if I could/ were able to speak Mandarin.
6 If I had more time, I would do more sport.
7 If I didn't have a television, I would read more books.
8 If you were famous, how would your life change?

5

2 If the restaurant wasn't so expensive, we would eat there.
3 If you watered the garden, it would look good.
4 If I had Jodie's number, I would call her.
5 If we had enough money, we could buy our own house.
6 If I had some food in the house, I would invite you in for lunch.
7 If I practised every day, I'd be good at the guitar.
8 If I didn't spend so much time answering my email, I would finish my other work.
9 If the flights weren't so expensive, we would visit very often.
10 If I wasn't so late, I would walk slowly.

6

2 thoughts 3 YouTube 4 people/ fans/viewers 5 fake 6 actress 7 friend

7

1 T 2 F 3 T 4 F 5 T 6 T 7 F 8 F

8

1 don't let 2 keep to yourself 3 surprised 4 not real 5 crazy

9A

Introduction/Early life

b, i, c, g

Career

l, e, j, k, a

Personal life

f, d, h

12.3

1

1 got 2 rented 3 recommended 4 organised 5 invited 6 booked

2

1 g 2 d 3 a 4 f 5 b 6 c 7 e

3

1 would like 2 be possible 3 able to 4 you recommend 5 Shall I 6 want me 7 like me

4

1 give 2 on 3 a 4 on

5A

1 C 2 B 3 A

B

	1	2	3
1 What do the customers want?	a bus tour of the city	to change seats	a table for two
2 Do they get what they want?	yes	no	yes

REVIEW AND CHECK 4

1

2 What's it like 3 Do you like 4 What's he like 5 Do you like 6 What's the (weather) like

2

1 safe 2 pollution 3 transport 4 traffic 5 nightlife 6 buildings 7 polite 8 crime

3

2 works 3 arrived 4 found 5 was hidden 6 gave 7 were told 8 were asked 9 gave 10 left 11 is not found

4

1 service 2 fine 3 shoplifting 4 fraud 5 thief 6 speeding 7 graffiti 8 driving

5

1 've just done
2 haven't asked (him) yet
3 've already paid
4 've (only) just started
5 has just brought
6 've just finished

6

1 crashed 2 faulty 3 text 4 webpage 5 search 6 virus 7 email 8 online

7

1 would 2 will 3 knew 4 will 5 was 6 will 7 get 8 left

8

1 b 2 b 3 a 4 a 5 b 6 b

9

2 successful 3 politician 4 helpful 5 wonderful 6 photographer

10

1 Suzie told to me that they wanted to move house.
2 We said told her that we wouldn't be long.
3 I called a taxi, but they told me they were busy.
4 They asked to move to a different table, but the waitress said told them that it wasn't possible.
5 My sister worked at the school, but last week they told she her to look for another job.
6 'It was a terrible journey,' the old man told said. 'I thought it would never end.'

11

2 comedy 3 horror 4 action 5 historical 6 science fiction

12

1 Could you help, There's a problem, I'm sorry about that
2 Excuse me, could I speak to, I'm afraid I have, there's nothing we can do
3 Could you recommend, Certainly, Would you like me to, No problem

TEST

1 b 2 c 3 a 4 b 5 c 6 c 7 a 8 b 9 b 10 a 11 c 12 b 13 b 14 b 15 c 16 a 17 c 18 a 19 b 20 a 21 c 22 a 23 c 24 a 25 c 26 c 27 a 28 b 29 b 30 c

Pearson Education Limited
Edinburgh Gate
Harlow
Essex CM20 2JE
England
and Associated Companies throughout the
world.

www.pearsonelt.com

© Pearson Education Limited 2011

The right of Antonia Clare and JJ Wilson
to be identified as authors of this Work has
been asserted by them in accordance with the
Copyright, Designs and Patents Act 1988.

First published 2011
Sixth impression 2015

ISBN: 978-1-40825-951-1

Set in Gill Sans Book 9.75/11.5
Printed in Malaysia (CTP-VVP)

Acknowledgements
The publisher would like to thank the following
for their kind permission to reproduce their
photographs:

(Key: b-bottom; c-centre; l-left; r-right; t-top)

Alamy Images: Fancy 66bl; Roussel Bernard
60cr; Corbis: Bettmann 24cr; Christophe
Boisvieux 18br; Christopher Felver 72tr; David
Moir/Reuters 43b; Gonzalo Fuentes/Reuters
24br; James Leynse 44c; MC Pherson Colin/
Sygma 47cl; Neal Preston 44b; Peter M. Fisher
34br; Steve Schapiro 44cl; WWD/Conde Nast
24tr; Getty Images: WireImage / Jon Furniss
47bl; iStockphoto: Lya Cattel 15br; Elmarie
Viljoen 19br; ezinigami 52bl; g_studio 33bl;
Jacom Stephens 6b; Jeremy Edwards 59b;
Rafal Belzowski 51tr; Robert Plotz 69cl; S.
Greg Panosian 60tr; Terraxplorer 60br; Willie
B. Thomas 33cl; Jupiter Unlimited: Stockxpert
16tl, 68br; Thinkstock Images 64cr, 66cl;
Reuters:Miguel Vidal 65tl; Rex Features:
BEI / Alex Berliner 72tc; Stewart Cook 47tl;
shutterstock: Stephen Finn 16tr; Wallenrock 33tl

All other images © Pearson Education

Picture Research by: Ann Thomson

Every effort has been made to trace the
copyright holders and we apologise in
advance for any unintentional omissions. We
would be pleased to insert the appropriate
acknowledgement in any subsequent edition of
this publication